JACOB'S GHETTO

SCRIPT NOVEL®

*You're not the product
of your environment.*

TRAVIS PEARLER

SCRIPT NOVEL®
PUBLISHING

Library of Congress Control Number: 2019910199

Printed in the United States of America. Published in Indianapolis by Script Novel an imprint of Script Novel Publishing. First Printing, 2019

Contact: www.TravisPeagler.com, via TravisWriter@TravisPeagler.com

Book Cover Design by: Levente Farkas

ISBN: 978-1-7325635-2-0 (Paperback)
ISBN: 978-1-7325635-3-7 (Hardback)
ISBN: 978-1-7325635-4-4 (Ebook)

WHAT IS SCRIPT NOVEL®?

TRAVIS *(all smiles)*: Script Novel is a new book style I've come up with. It's sort of an adaptation of a movie script/ screenplay and a traditional novel. So, in essence, you're reading a real script that's been formatted to the likeness of a traditional book, but still has similarities with a real script… It's also an easy read and easy on the eyes.

ACKNOWLEDGEMENTS

As I sit here pondering on all the people that have helped me along my writing journey, the first person that comes to mind is my cousin Chad. At the age of seventeen years old, my cousin introduced me to the world of writing screenplays. I can't say that I would be where I am in my writing career today, or if I would've started writing at all, so for that, I say, thank you!

The second person I must thank is my beautiful soul, my mother. As a young teenager, my mother never pressed me to get a job, because she knew I was passionate about writing, and she gave me the space and time I needed to work on my craft. So, Mom, thanks for always believing in me and being supportive of my dream, emotionally and financially.

Lastly, I need to thank my awesome wife, Stacey, for being so understanding, knowing that a writer needs to write. Thank you for giving me the space to do so. Also, my kids, Trais and Trinity, for giving me the fuel I need when I'm too tired to write anything; your bright eyes and faces always brighten my day. The cherry on top is seeing how proud they are of me, writing my novels and telling my stories. Daddy loves you!

Above it all, I give God the glory always. Thank you for blessing me with such a remarkable talent... Amen!

PREFACE

What would you do if you were born with the cards of life stacked against you? Not being born into a family of wealth, good jobs, or having both parents in the home to raise you. A post-era of Government cheese and still no solution to address poverty in this country that we call great and land of the free. Many times, the ramifications of unfortunate living conditions are not felt or truly understood until one becomes of age to know better. Around the United States and world, there are many Jacobs with different names that are born into God-forsaken situations and are forced to choose their path in life; they either become a product of their environment, which I'm sure would involve committing malicious acts to survive or figure out a way to escape it by taking the hard clean road to success.

The story titled Jacob's Ghetto is a fictional one, but yet a very relatable and real story in the sense of how Jacob decided to go against the grain of his downtrodden community and vowed to make it with his beloved talent of writing. Even though his talent was birthed from a place of pain and torment, he desperately tried to wield it to change his living condition and trajectory in life.

There are many exceptionally gifted young people in the ghettos across this country and I pray that they not only discover their talent, but also find a way to use it to escape and maybe one day change the harsh environment that they came from.

FADE IN:

INT. APARTMENT - BATHROOM -- EVENING

DIRTY

KEISHA, a diseased-looking woman in her early 30s bustles out of the BATHROOM.

LIVING ROOM AREA

An elastic band tied tightly around her arm. A needle dangles from her vein. Needless to say, Keisha is obviously a drug addict. She stumbles about. Collapses on the sofa.

EXT. SIDEWALK -- CONTINUOUS

POVERTY-STRICKEN NEIGHBORHOOD A.K.A THE GHETTO

A young ten-year-old boy sporting a Red Chicago Cubs baseball cap. It's flipped backward, the way he likes it. His blue backpack flung over both shoulders.

He walks along with a purpose. A mission. With each step, he looks over his shoulders. Right, then left. He walks right over a spot on the concrete where a body was outlined in chalk. The fresh blood splatter tells the end of the story.

He's not surprised; he's almost immune to the senseless violence, but the love in his heart won't let him succumb to it completely. Unfortunately, this is normal scenery; more than a rough neighborhood; this is a place where people die young.

INT. APARTMENT -- CONTINUOUS

JACOB, Keisha's ten-year-old son, slowly enters the apartment. He is cautious as he shuts the door. He quickly places his key into his pocket.

Jacob takes a deep sigh as he clears some clutter from the hallway.

LIVING ROOM

KEISHA

(slurred speech)

Jacob. Is that you, boy?!

Jacob drops his head and enters the living room. He quietly walks over and pulls the needle from Keisha's arm. He unties the elastic band. Tosses it aside. Sadly, he's used to this routine. He's forced to burden a chore no kid should ever have.

KEISHA

Jacob. Jacob baby?

JACOB

Yes, Mom!

KEISHA

Why didn't you answer when I called you?

JACOB

Goodnight, Mom.

Jacob lifts Keisha's legs, and places them on the sofa. He walks over, and turns off the television.

In the Kitchen, Jacob stands before the refrigerator. He braces himself... Slowly, he opens the door. The refrigerator is EMPTY. Only a bottle of ketchup and mustard remains.

JACOB (CONT'D)

Why do I even bother?

Jacob SLAMs the refrigerator door and walks over to the kitchen sink where he's rigged the broken faucet handle with a pair of pliers. The faucet is broken, but has a slow drip. There sits a cup underneath the dripping faucet. It's a little more than half-way full. Jacob squeezes the pliers as hard as he can and wiggles it about. He manages to get several more drops of water. Without any more hesitation, he hurries and drinks the cup of water, then places the cup back underneath the faucet.

INT. JACOB'S BEDROOM -- CONTINUOUS

Jacob turns on the light, walks over, and sits down on the bed. He removes his backpack. Pulls out a banana and munches down. He's extremely hungry.

Jacob pulls his notebook from his backpack and writes: "If I could cry for my mother, I would, but I cannot, as my jar of tears for her is empty."

Jacob begins to sob quietly. He continues to write: "But who cries for me, innocent Jacob? I'm the only one who cries for myself. I'm sorry for myself."

Suddenly, a series of loud gun BLASTs can be heard outside. Unshaken, Jacob rolls off his bed, falls to his knees, and bows his head for prayer.

DISSOLVE TO:

EXT. JACOB'S APARTMENT -- MORNING

Dressed for school, Jacob pushes through the door and finds his best friend, KENNY, 8, squatting on the steps. Kenny, a charming-lovable boy with a smile that engulfs his face.

JACOB

How long have you been sitting out here, Kenny?

KENNY

Oh, maybe about ten-minutes.

JACOB

How come you didn't knock on the door?

Jacob skips down the steps and strides up the sidewalk. Kenny jumps up and quickly follows behind.

KENNY

I ain't crazy, man. The last time I knocked on your door, your momma hit me in the head with a frying pan.

Jacob laughs.

KENNY (CONT'D)

That ain't funny, Jacob. I had to get one-half of a stitch put on the side of my head.

JACOB

You're right. I'm sorry. Sometimes I have to laugh, even when I wanna cry, you know?

Kenny pats Jacob on the back.

KENNY

It's okay, Jacob, because you're smart, Jacob. You're like a genius, almost. You're gonna make it out of this ghetto here -- for both of us.

A winsome smile compliments Jacob's face.

KENNY (CONT'D)

We both know I'm not that smart. So, I'm really counting on you, Jacob.

JACOB

Yea, me too.

But Jacob's face tells another story. He's uncertain. His countenance is of a prisoner serving a life sentence.

KENNY

What's wrong, Jacob? I'm counting on you, Negro.

Somberly, smiling just a tad.

JACOB

I got you, Kenny.

(beat)

You know you're deep in the hood, when they don't even send buses in the morning to pick you up for school.

Kenny points to a condemned-abandoned apartment building that has graffiti spray-painted on the side of it. INSERT GRAFFITI: "City of Ashes."

They both sorrowfully shake their head, without a word spoken; they both recognize the reflection of despair in each other's eyes.

CUT TO:

INT. RAVEN ELEMENTARY SCHOOL -- LATER

HALLWAY

Jacob and Kenny bump fists as they break off in opposite directions toward their classroom.

JACOB'S CLASSROOM

NOISY, a bunch of hyperactive kids running about.

Jacob takes off his hat, hangs his backpack on his chair, and sits down. MISS COLLINS, 30s, stands quietly in front of the class with a stack of papers in her hand.

Miss Collins is one beautiful BLACK WOMAN. The way she looks upon her students, you know they're her top priority.

MISS COLLINS

Unt un!!!

The rest of the students quickly take their seats.

MISS COLLINS (CONT'D)

Good morning class!

THE ENTIRE CLASS

Good morning, Miss Collins!

MISS COLLINS

(smiling)

> First off, I would like to start the
> day by announcing your test scores.
> And... That everyone passed with flying
> colors!

The entire class cheers with excitement.

MISS COLLINS (CONT'D)

> Needless to say, that you guys know how
> crucial, and important it was for all
> of you to pass this test in order to
> move on to the next grade.

Miss Collins happily walks about and passes out the test scores.

MISS COLLINS (CONT'D)

> I'm so proud of you guys. I told you
> hard work pays off. I will keep my
> promise as well by ordering pizza for
> lunch today.

Everyone yells out with excitement. Miss Collins hands Jacob his test score.

MISS COLLINS (CONT'D)

> Perfect score, as usual, Jacob.
> Good job.

Jacob doesn't appear to be enthused. Miss Collins notices his colorless reaction.

JACOB

> Thank you.

MISS COLLINS

> What's wrong? You should be happy; you
> can't score any higher.

JACOB

I know,

(now whispering)

I hate my life.

MISS COLLINS

What? "I hate my life." Don't talk like that, Jacob.

JACOB

Are you serious?

MISS COLLINS

Jacob, we will discuss this in private, okay?

Jacob blocks out Miss Collins -- doesn't respond.

EXT. RAVEN ELEMENTARY SCHOOL -- MOMENTS LATER

SITTING AREA

Miss Collins sits down with Jacob.

MISS COLLINS

What's going on with you, Jacob? Why do you hate your life?

JACOB

Miss Collins, is your mother a Junkie?

MISS COLLINS

No, Jacob. Why are you --

JACOB

-- Because my mother is a Junkie.
She's a crackhead, cokehead, and she
uses heroin. Did I mention she's an
alcoholic too?

Miss Collins tries to console Jacob.

MISS COLLINS

I'm sorry to hear that, Jacob, but I
think I know where you are going with
all of this.

JACOB

No, I don't think you do. I'm tired of
my life. I'm tired of coming home every
day and not having anything to eat, and
not knowing if she's gonna be lying
on the floor dead. I have to ask Mr.
Tony at the corner market for a banana
every day so I can have something to
eat every night. Someone gets killed
in my neighborhood every day. Do you
hear me? Every day, someone gets
murdered! Every night, I fall asleep
to the sound of gunshots.

(beat)

I don't even know what keeps me going,
or how I even manage to get good grades.
I don't even study half the time.

Miss Collins is conflicted. Jacob, a mere boy expressing
himself much like an adult.

MISS COLLINS

You don't study?

JACOB

No, I spend all my free time writing.

MISS COLLINS

Why? What do you write about?

JACOB

My life mostly. I write as if I'm
writing a story, except it's all true.
I don't know what it is, but I feel free
when I write.

MISS COLLINS

Then that's what you were born to do.
You're supposed to be a writer --

JACOB

-- I'm no real writer. I just jot down
the torments of my chaotic life to pass
the time by, before someone murders me.

Miss Collins' mouth moves about, but she is utterly lost for words. Tears slowly begin to stream down her face. She suddenly regains her composure.

MISS COLLINS

No, Jacob. Listen to me - whatever
gives us freedom in this life is what
we're supposed to do, and I believe
that's God's will for us. I feel
free when I am teaching, and that's
why I love it so much. God has
blessed you

```
with a tremendous talent.  So, hang on,
sweetie and God will take you where
you want to go in life.  Life is like
a big-old bully, so be ready to fight
every step of the way.  I will help you
with whatever I can, but you've got to
start thinking positive.  Even when
there's nothing positive in sight.
```

With all sincerity - she rubs the back of Jacob's head. Jacob stares at her intently. He knows that he can trust her.

MISS COLLINS (CONT'D)

```
Starting with a packed lunch for dinner.
Every day, I will place a lunch in your
backpack so you can have something to
eat for dinner.  And don't worry, I will
do it when no one is around, okay?  I
don't want you being embarrassed.  This
will be our little secret.
```

Jacob hugs Miss Collins.

JACOB

```
Thank you, Miss Collins.  I wish you
were my mom, sometimes.
```

Miss Collins stares sorrowfully off into the distance.

EXT. CRACK HOUSE -- EVENING

Lavish custom painted Cadillac Escalades, Monte Carlos, and other cars sit on the side of the street.

Gang leader GINO, 30s, stands out front drinking and smoking with 30 of his gang members including his second in command, JA'HEVE, 20s.

Bald, Gino stands six-foot-three with a muscular build, very well-dressed. He has a SPIDER-WEB-like SCAR on the back of his head. Ja'heve is shorter in stature with a slender build. He possesses the look of a sadistic savage. He does not respect life, not even his own.

GINO

(to the gangsters)

> Don't none of you killers ever forget,
> this is the Circle --

Gino throws up the CIRCLE gang sign.

GINO (CONT'D)

> The Circle is everlasting, and Circle
> niggas don't bow down to nobody.

The crowd of GANGSTERS shows their allegiance by throwing up the CIRCLE gang sign.

GINO (CONT'D)

> We run more than half the city and soon
> we will run all of it.

(now pointing to the cars)

> I told yawl in the beginning if I eat,
> we all eat. Let's keep it gangster,
> niggas.

Gino pulls out a pretty CHROME PLATED 9MM pistol and fires his entire clip into the air. After the final shot, everyone SHOUTS, "Amen."

Out of nowhere, a police cruiser pulls on the street alongside them. None of them seems to care, as they continue to smoke and drink.

Ja'heve looks over at Gino. Gino signals him to go over to the police cruiser. Ja'heve walks up on the cop car. Two obese white cops are sandwiched inside. Ja'heve notices a box of Krispy Cremes sitting on the dash.

OBESE COP #1

Ja'heve, my man, what's up, bro? How many drive-bys you do today?

Obese Cop #2 cracks up laughing. Ja'heve continues to look stone-faced.

JA'HEVE

Why don't you two pork bellies let me kill you now and take you out of your misery? Better to die with a bullet than by a fat attack.

OBESE COP #1

(laughing)

Fat attack! That's hilarious. No, I'm good - the doc says once I gain another fifty pounds, my insurance will pay for my gastric bypass --

Obese Cop#1 grabs a donut and shoves it down his throat.

OBESE COP #1 (CONT'D)

-- So, it's all good "Baba baby."

(chuckling)

That was Biggie Smalls, right!? Hey Baba baby!

OBESE COP #2

(rapping)

"If ya don't know, now ya know Nig --"

JA'HEVE

-- Yo! Don't say it, or you two fat motherfuckas be deaded up in this bitch.

Ja'heve pulls out a stack of hundred dollar bills out of his waistband and tosses it into the car.

JA'HEVE (CONT'D)

Get the hell on!

OBESE COP #1

(nervously)

You got it. Thanks.

EXT. CRACK HOUSE -- LATER

Jacob and Kenny pass by. A few gang members are posted up on the porch. As Jacob is about to turn his head to look at the gang members, Kenny stops him.

KENNY

No, Jacob, don't look up at'em.

JACOB

Why?

KENNY

It's a sign of disrespect; they might kill you.

JACOB

Yea, right!

KENNY

No. I'm serious, Jacob, my brother used to be part of the "Circle" before he got killed. They don't play, Jacob.

Gang member #1 steps off the porch, walking behind Jacob and Kenny. Gang member #2 paces behind him.

GANG MEMBER #1

Hey, you little homie in the red hat, come over here.

Frightened, Kenny looks over at Jacob.

KENNY

(whisper)

Run, Jacob, run!

JACOB

No, it's cool. Don't be afraid.

Jacob and Kenny stops, and turn around.

GANG MEMBER #1

You little joints, know where y'all at?

JACOB

We just stay around the corner.

GANG MEMBER #2

How old are yawl?

JACOB

I'm ten, and he's eight.

GANG MEMBER #1

Good, yawl just the right age to join the Circle.

JACOB

Thanks, but no thanks. Come on, Kenny.

Jacob and Kenny attempt to turn and walk away.

GANG MEMBER #1

> Little nigga, is you crazy? I'm still
> talking to your little ass. "Thanks,
> but no thanks?" Who the hell do you
> think you talking to?

Suddenly, Ja'heve appears out of nowhere and puts a 9mm to Jacob's head. Kenny starts to cry. Jacob is surprisingly calm.

JA'HEVE

> You scared now, huh?

JACOB

> No, why should I?

Ja'heve looks surprised.

JA'HEVE

> Give me one reason why I shouldn't blow
> your fuckin' brains out, buckwheat?

JACOB

(talking slowly)

> How about I give you one reason why you
> should?

Jacob begins to tremble with anger, as a tear strolls down his cheek.

JACOB (CONT'D)

> I hate my life, so why don't you go
> ahead and pull the trigger? Child-
> killer, you'll be doing me a favor.

The two other gang member look on in disbelief. Ja'heve smiles with delight.

JA'HEVE

Either you a brave little nigga, or you got that Autisy, Autism, or some shit.

Smiling, Ja'heve cocks back the gun, then presses it on Jacob's temple.

JA'HEVE (CONT'D)

Your wish is my command, young blood.

Gino appears with four other gang members.

GINO

Ja, you slipping, or what? You can't recognize a brave heart when you see one?

Ja'heve quickly places the gun back into his waistband.

JA'HEVE

Gino!

GINO

Go ahead and run on home, Jacob.

JACOB

How do you know my name?

Gino winks at Jacob.

GINO

Run on home.

Jacob and Kenny take off running.

KENNY

```
We need to take you to the hospital to
get your head examined, Jacob.  I think
you might be crazy.
```

Jacob laughs as he wipes a tear from his eye.

BACK TO GINO AND JA'HEVE

GINO

```
Ja, don't ever let me catch you putting
a gun to that boy's head.  The Circle
don't roll like that.  We were all
that age once.  Remember that.
Without a code, we ain't shit.
```

Gino and some other gang members hop in a BULLET-PROOF SUV and drive off.

Ja'heve watches Jacob fade off into the distance.

JA'HEVE
(whispering)
```
I'm gonna kill Jacob!
```

CUT TO:

INT. JACOB'S LIVING ROOM -- NIGHT

Jacob enters the living room and sees his mother lying on the couch with her eyes closed.

KEISHA

```
Jacob, is that you, baby?
```

JACOB

Yea.

Keisha is sleep-deprived. She can barely keep her eyes open.

KEISHA

How was school today?

JACOB

It was okay.

KEISHA

Did you learn your ABCs yet?

JACOB

Mom, I'm in the fifth grade.

KEISHA

Okay! Well, damn it, did that teacher
bitch teach you your ABCs and shit?

Jacob looks confused, as he doesn't respond. Tiptoes off into his room.

INT. BEDROOM

Jacob quietly closes the door. He knows it's all drug talk; he's heard the cuss word symphony before.

KEISHA (O.S.)

Jacob! Jacob! I'm going beat the hell
out of you, when I wake up.

Jacob takes the lunch out of his backpack and eats. He lies back on the bed.

JACOB

(elated)

> Thank you, Miss Collins. My stomach
> won't be growling tonight.

Jacob looks over - notices a new outfit and pair of shoes lying across his dresser. He perks up and rushes to look at his new clothes.

JACOB (CONT'D)

> This is tight!

Jacob quickly tries on his new clothes. Dances around. Takes them off, and folds them up neatly, placing them on the dresser. He walks over to his bed and grabs his pen and note pad from his backpack.

Jacob fluffs his pillow, then lies down. He thinks for a moment, then writes.

JACOB (CONT'D)

> "I almost got killed today. In a way,
> I guess I sort of wanted to die, but
> deep down, I knew that God would not
> let that happen. I don't know that much
> about God, Heaven, evil and all that
> kind of stuff, but I do believe. That's
> why I pray every night. In a strange
> sense, I feel as if someone is always
> watching me. I guess in a way I feel
> like someone is protecting me from this
> ungodly place."

Jacob closes his notebook, then kills the light. He pulls his blanket over his head as he looks out of his window.

Jacob stares at a flashing RED LIGHT on top of a hospital building off in the distance.

JACOB (CONT'D)

God, I know you can hear me, because you're God, right? ... Well, God, I know I'm young and all, but around here, age ain't nothing but a number. Kids my age get killed almost every week on the Southside of Chicago. I just wanted to ask you if you could send me a Guardian angel to protect me from all the violence and death that fill the streets. Because you see --

Jacob breaks down crying.

JACOB (CONT'D)

-- I, I lied when I told that gangbanger that I didn't care about my life, because I do. I'm just afraid that I won't be able to live it.

Jacob wipes his tears with his pillowcase.

JACOB (CONT'D)

So, if you could spare one of your Angels, I would appreciate it.

EXT. SIDEWALK -- DAY

Jacob and Kenny tread up the road. Jacob sports his new outfit and it shows. He grins from ear to ear. Kenny notices. GIGGLES!

JACOB

What?

KENNY

Somebody is happy because they got some
new clothes, huh?!

Jacob glances down at his shoes. Looks at Kenny with a
pillsbury smile.

JACOB

A little.

KENNY

Have you found out who has been sending
you all the clothes yet?

Jacob ponders in deep thought.

JACOB

No, not yet.

KENNY

Your mom's not telling the truth, Jacob.
She knows where all the clothes are
coming from.

Kenny attempts to say something more, then decides not to.

JACOB

Say what you were gonna say.

Kenny looks a bit cautious.

KENNY

Well, I don't want this to come out
wrong. But if it does, you have to
promise not to be mad at me.

(beat)

Promise?

JACOB

Promise.

Jacob looks very interested as he waits.

KENNY

You don't think your mom is turning tricks for those clothes, do you?

Kenny braces back. Not sure how to prepare for Jacob's reaction. Jacob doesn't show any signs of animosity.

JACOB

If she is, I hope she starts tricking for some groceries too.

Kenny looks relieved as he and Jacob laugh.

JACOB (CONT'D)

I'm serious, there's never any food in the house. I can't even make a mustard sandwich, because we ain't got no bread.

KENNY

(laughing)

I can't either, half the time. I steal all my food from the cafeteria.

JACOB

Well, at least you're stealing for a good cause.

KENNY

What good cause?

JACOB

To stay alive.

KENNY

Oh yea. Right! ... So where are you
taking me to, Jacob?

Suddenly, BRITTANY, a girl Jacob has a crush on, walks up behind them.

BRITTANY

Yeah, Jacob, what's the big surprise? I
wanna go too.

Jacob is surprised to see Brittany.

JACOB

Uh sure, where did you come from? You
should get to school.

BRITTANY

I could say the same for you two.

KENNY

She's got a point there, Jacob buddy.

JACOB

Ok cool, just don't clown me, when we
get there.

BRITTANY

I promise!

CUT TO:

INT. TRAIN - MOMENTS LATER

They all head for the very back of the train.

BRITTANY

So, how often do you do whatever it is
that you're doing, Jacob?

JACOB

At least twice a year. For
motivation, I have to.

Kenny looks at Brittany and shrugs his shoulders.

BRITTANY

Ok, now I'm really confused.

They all take a seat. Kenny notices a folded-up piece of
paper. Being the curious little boy that he is, he quickly grabs
it and opens it up. Kenny can't read that well, but he gives it
his best shot.

KENNY

Ok, let's see what this says. It says
here, "First Annual, the first annual
writing." Here, Jacob, this is for you,
it's about writing.

Kenny hands Jacob the paper. Jacob quickly reads the paper.
It's an entry form.

JACOB

"Redridge Publishing Company's First
Annual Writing Competition. Open to all
genres of fiction and non-fiction literary
works. If under eighteen years of age,
must have parents' permission to enter.
First-place winner will receive a fifty-
thousand-dollar cash prize and a book
deal."

A dim light of hope now shines bright inside of Jacob. He's suddenly filled with purpose and a goal in life. He's going to enter.

KENNY

What do you think, you're going to enter this, right?

JACOB

Oh yeah! This can be my ticket out.

BRITTANY

I didn't know you were a writer, Jacob. You should enter, you never know!

Brittany reaches out for the entry form; Jacob hands it to her. She reads the contest info quietly.

JACOB

I'm not really. I just write in my notebook a lot.

KENNY

I knew you would make good use of it, Jacob; you write all the time.

JACOB

Thanks, Kenny! Wow, this is amazing! I never knew how much money people made from writing books, but this is a lot of money.

KENNY

You'll be rich, Jacob; just buy me some Jordan shoes when you win. I'll be happy; boy, I'll be so happy.

Kenny glances down at his busted shoes.

JACOB

I'll do better than that, Kenny.

Brittany hands the contest form back to Jacob. Jacob hurries and puts it inside his backpack. The train slowly comes to a halt. Jacob hurries for the exit.

JACOB (CONT'D)

Come on y'all.

They all exit the train with excitement. Then, suddenly, Brittany and Kenny start to look a little worried. The area is too nice and clean looking. That shouldn't be a bad thing, but it makes them very uncomfortable - nice business opposed to run-down and boarded-up ones. People zip pass in their nice cars, traffic is heavy as people commute to work.

BRITTANY

Jacob, where are we, where are we going?

JACOB

We're on the Northside now. Just follow me; we'll be there in five minutes or so.

They both quickly follow behind Jacob.

KENNY

I'm not sure about this, Jacob. We don't know, like what gangs are around here you know. We don't know what to expect.

BRITTANY

Yeah, Jacob.

JACOB

(laughing)

> Look around you. We're not in the hood
> anymore yawl. We're good; we're on the
> wealthy side of Chicago now.

KENNY

> Wealthy, what's that?

JACOB

> People that are well-off. People that
> have a lot of money and own their own
> properties and stuff... Just a little
> further up the road, guys.

After walking further up the road, they finally reach, "Stone Hedge Village," a wealthy community with houses ranging in the mid three-hundred-thousand dollar range. The immense community sign in front of the main entrance is beautifully decorated with colorful bushes and an assortment of flowers.

BRITTANY

> Wow, look at the beautiful flowers. I've
> never seen flowers like this before. I
> mean on TV, yeah, but not in person.

Jacob walks over and picks a Purple Tulip from the flower garden and gives it to Brittany.

JACOB

> For you!

Brittany blushes.

BRITTANY

> Thank you, Jacob.

Kenny laughs.

KENNY

Ahhh, thank you, Jacob.

Jacob smiles as he playfully pushes Kenny in the back.

JACOB

Come on!

They all follow Jacob into the neighborhood. Jacob points to different houses that he likes. A few white people exit their home; they watch cautiously as they get in their vehicles and head off to work. You can see one person drive past while calling someone on their cell phone.

Jacob finally takes a seat on the sidewalk curb. Brittany and Kenny sit down beside him. Jacob looks at peace here; it's no secret that this is his happy place. No violence, no gunshots, he can relax here. He stares off into the distance.

Brittany and Kenny are in awe as well. They finally understand why Jacob likes this neighborhood so much. No liquor stores, no yellow police tape decorations, and no portraits of bodies outlined in chalk along the pavement.

BRITTANY

Now, I see what you mean, Jacob.

JACOB

What's that?

BRITTANY

Your motivation. I get it now. Seeing a nice neighborhood like this gives you something to look forward to when you get older. Proof that not every neighborhood is a raggedy ghetto.

JACOB

Exactly, this is what's up, right. I feel so...

Suddenly, a Police car rolls up and lays on the siren a few times then stops. A White and Hispanic officer Pratt and Reyes exit the police car.

OFFICER PRATT

I'll let you handle the delinquents, Reyes.

OFFICER REYES

Really, Pratt, it's like that.

OFFICER PRATT

I'm just saying; you probably can relate better to them better than I can.

OFFICER REYES

I guess you got a point, but don't call them "delinquents," man. Let's see what's going on first.

OFFICER PRATT

My bad, my bad, I apologize.

They both approach the kids. Kenny becomes anxious; Jacob grabs his arm before he can take off running.

JACOB

Be cool, Kenny; we didn't do anything wrong, relax.

OFFICER REYES

Hey guys, we got a call of suspicious activity in this neighborhood. Y'all know anything about that?

JACOB

Good morning, officers. Since when did walking and admiring homes become suspicious activity?

Both officers are caught off guard with Jacob's response and diction. Brittany snickers quietly.

OFFICER REYES

Ugh, how old are you, kid, what's your name?

JACOB

I'm ten, and my name is Jacob.

OFFICER PRATT

Only ten, you say?

OFFICER REYES

I got this, remember.

OFFICER PRATT

Alright, my bad.

OFFICER REYES

Okay, you're right, admiring homes is not a crime, but could be considered suspicious activity.

JACOB

Is it suspicious activity when a realtor is canvassing a neighborhood for new homes to market?

Officer Pratt bursts out laughing.

OFFICER PRATT

He got you there, partner; this kid is
smart as shit.

OFFICER REYES

Language, please.

OFFICER PRATT

You're right, my bad.

Officer Reyes thinks for a moment before responding. Jacob
and crew wait patiently.

OFFICER REYES

Ok, Jacob, that's a little different
because that's a realtor, that's their
job.

JACOB

But they don't drive around with, "I'm
a Realtor," sign on their vehicle, do
they? So, they could be suspicious too,
right?

Officer Reyes, scratching his head.

OFFICER REYES

Ok, you got me, Jacob.

Officer Reyes looks down at his watch.

OFFICER REYES (CONT'D)

Okay, but it's seven-forty-five a.m. in
the morning, why aren't you kids in
school?

JACOB

Now, you got me.

Officer Reyes smiles.

JACOB (CONT'D)

I really don't have a good excuse. I needed to get a few moments out the ghetto where we live to daydream and find some motivation to keep going. Life is hard for kids like us. We're surrounded by filth and live in filth. Coming here twice a year helps me escape.

Both officers get choked up unexpectedly.

OFFICER REYES

It's totally worth it, Jacob. It's totally worth it. I mean, I don't' condone skipping school, but I totally understand... Let me guess, you kids are from the Southside.

They all nod their head.

OFFICER PRATT

Let's get these kids to school, huh?

OFFICER REYES

Yeah, right. Jacob, we're going to give you all a ride to school, okay?

Suddenly, an erratic angry lady approaches.

ANGRY LADY

I want these little junior hoodlums arrested.

BRITTANY

Who're you calling a hoodlum?

OFFICER REYES

Arrested for what, ma'am? They're just
enjoying your beautiful neighborhood.

The angry lady notices the purple tulip Brittany is holding.

ANGRY LADY

For thief.

OFFICER REYES

Thief? What did they steal, ma'am?

ANGRY LADY

That flower right there. That tulip,
they stole it from our flower garden at
the entrance of the neighborhood.

Both officers look at each other in disbelief.

OFFICER PRATT

Are you serious, Lady? You want these
kids to go to jail over a flower?

The lady knows she's being irrational, but sticks with it.

ANGRY LADY

Uhhh, yes, yes, I do.

Officer Pratt pulls out his wallet and hands the lady a ten-dollar bill.

OFFICER PRATT

Here, will this cover a single flower?
I bet if one of your kids would have
brought you home a flower, you
would've thought it was the sweetest
thing ever! Right?

The lady snatches the ten-dollar bill and walks off.

OFFICER REYES

Dear Lord, you can't make this stuff up, can you?

OFFICER PRATT

Not ever.

OFFICER REYES

Come on, gang, let's get you all to school.

They all load up into the police car. Kenny is all smiles, as he's about to experience a field trip he's never had before. So exciting to ride in a police car without going to jail. Officer Reyes pulls off.

INT. POLICE CAR - CONTINUOUS

OFFICER REYES

Hey, have you guys eaten breakfast yet?

KENNY

Breakfast, what's that?

JACOB

No, sir; no, we have not, Officer Reyes.

OFFICER REYES

What do you say, partner? Let's get these kids some food before we drop them off.

OFFICER PRATT

Sounds good to me.

OFFICER REYES

Ok, we're going to get you guys some
food. How does McDonald's sound?

KENNY

Heck yea, I love McDonald's.

Everyone agrees. Officer Reyes finds a McDonalds and
pulls up to the drive-thru and orders food. Jacob, Kenny, and
Brittany are really excited. Officer Reyes drives to the pick-
up window and pays for all the food. He pulls forward a little
and rolls down the window so the kids can get their food.
They quickly ration out the food amongst each other with
smiles and quickly eat.

Officer Reyes pulls off as he and Officer Pratt smile as they
watch the kids eat through the rear-view mirror.

DISSOLVE TO:

**EXT. RAVEN ELEMENTARY SCHOOL - MOMENTS
LATER**

Officer Reyes pulls up in front of the school, quickly exits the
car, and lets the kids out.

OFFICER REYES

Don't worry about the trash, guys, we'll
take care of it.

BRITTANY

Thank you!

KENNY

Thanks!

JACOB

Thanks, Officer Reyes and Officer Pratt.

They all quickly rush inside.

OFFICER REYES

Hey, Jacob, come here a minute.

Jacob runs back. Officer Reyes pulls out his wallet and hands Jacob his business card. Officer Reyes shakes Jacob's hand.

OFFICER REYES (CONT'D)

Jacob, if you need anything, don't hesitate to call, ok?

JACOB

Ok, thanks!

CUT TO:

EXT. SIDEWALK - LATER

Jacob and Kenny are walking along talking and laughing. Suddenly, a SPEEDING BLACK Dodge Charger skids out in front of them. Startled, they both jump out of the way.

Ja'heve and two of his gang-goonies jump out of the car. Ja'heve pops his ashy knuckles as he steps in Jacob's face.

JA'HEVE

What's up, Jacob, the little badass? I been looking for you.

Jacob is not afraid. He remains calm. Ja'heve pulls back his shirt revealing his CHROME-PLATED PISTOL. Kenny cringes with fear. Jacob looks curiously up at the sky.

Ja'heve explodes with laughter.

JA'HEVE (CONT'D)

What, you looking for heaven, nigga?

Jacob ignores his comments as he continues to stare at the sky. Ja'heve is angered and reaches for his pistol. Kenny distracts him.

KENNY

Hey! I'll join your gang. Please, pick me instead; Jacob wouldn't make a good gang banger anyway.

Jacob glances over at Kenny in awe. He quickly shakes his head NO.

Ja'heve forgets about pulling his pistol. His eyes are now locked on Kenny.

JA'HEVE

Awl, you wanna be a Circle, huh?

KENNY

Yes!

The sinister grin slides across Ja'heve's face. The other gang members continue to look tough and poised. They show no change in their facial expression.

JA'HEVE

(excited)

Alright then, young blood. Number one, since your ass is too young, there won't be a beat in, but you will have to square off with other little niggas

like yourself. Ain't no softies in the
Circle, you understand?

Afraid for his life, Kenny nods his head.

JA'HEVE (CONT'D)
You gonna learn how to use these --

Putting up his fists, Ja'heve throws a few punches.

JA'HEVE (CONT'D)
And you will learn how to pop these
thangs.

Pointing to his PISTOL. Ja'heve hawks over at Jacob.

JA'HEVE (CONT'D)
You lucky nigga.

Ja'heve throws a gang-sign into the air.

JA'HEVE (CONT'D)
Let's roll.

All the gang members enter the car. Ja'heve grabs Kenny by
his collar and throws him inside. Kenny cries silently as he
glances back at Jacob.

Jacob is frozen stiff. CAN'T MOVE. He looks helpless as
the car SPEEDS off.

INT. MISS COLLINS' KITCHEN -- MORNING

Miss Collins takes a quick sip of her coffee. She grabs her
bag and purse, then heads out of the kitchen. Suddenly, she
stops as if she forgot something. She rushes back in and
grabs Jacob's lunch from the refrigerator.

EXT. MISS COLLINS' HOUSE -- CONTINUOUS

Miss Collins gets into her JETTA and drives off.

INT. SCHOOL'S BREAK ROOM -- LATER

Miss Collins sits quietly reading a Women's Health Magazine. PRINCIPAL DAILEY parades into the break room. White male, early 40s, conceited and conservative. Dailey acts as if he's God's gift to women.

Miss Collins pretends not to notice him. Continues to read.

PRINCIPAL DAILEY

Good afternoon, Miss Collins.

MISS COLLINS

Afternoon, Principal Dailey.

Principal Dailey does a goofy, suave type of pimp-walk towards the refrigerator. Grabs an orange juice, gently twists off the cap, and puts a straw in. Principal Dailey takes a few sips. He grabs a chair next to Miss Collins.

PRINCIPAL DAILEY

What're you reading, Mrs. Butterworth?

MISS COLLINS

Please! I'm not in the mood for your lame pick up lines, Principal Dailey.

Principal Dailey gulps a few sips of his drink.

PRINCIPAL DAILEY

It's cool, baby, I can dig it.

MISS COLLINS

You know I can report you to the
Superintendent, right?

PRINCIPAL DAILEY

Yes, I do, but I know you won't.

Miss Collins pushes the magazine aside.

MISS COLLINS

And why is that?

PRINCIPAL DAILEY

Because you know it's all just a little
harmless flirting. I'm never sexist
towards you and I've never laid a finger
on you, boo-boo. Besides, you know, as
well as I do, that I always make sure
that you and your students always have
everything you need.

MISS COLLINS

That is true and I appreciate that, but
please, just stop. I'm not interested.

PRINCIPAL DAILEY

I get it though! You're black, I'm
black --

MISS COLLINS

Excuse me!

PRINCIPAL DAILEY

I mean, you're black, I'm white.
Let's get together and make a little
cute mixed baby.

Miss Collins stands up and grabs her purse and magazine.

MISS COLLINS
(laughing)

Okay, there is something seriously wrong with you.

Miss Collins turns to walk out of the break room.

PRINCIPAL DAILEY

Aw, come on; he'll have a good grade of hair - with a curly afro.

INT. CLASSROOM -- LATER

Miss Collins stands anxiously in front of the class and looks up at the clock, which reads: 2:35.

MISS COLLINS

Are you guys sure you haven't seen Jacob today?

ENTIRE CLASS

Yes, Miss Collins!

MISS COLLINS

Okay, class, enjoy the rest of your day and be safe.

The school bell SOUNDS. All of the kids excitedly rush out.

CUT TO:

EXT. SCHOOL PARKING LOT -- EVENING

Miss Collins walks up to her car and pops the trunk. She places her bag in the trunk.

INT. CAR -- CONTINUOUS

Prances around and gets in the car. She starts the car and pulls off. After driving for a moment, Jacob rises from the back seat, stretching about.

MISS COLLINS

(startled)

> Jacob!

JACOB

> Hi, Miss Collins. What time is it?

Miss Collins hurries and pulls off to the side of the road.

MISS COLLINS

> It's late, that's what time it is.
> Jacob, are you okay? Why weren't you in
> school today? What are you doing in my
> car?

JACOB

> I'm sorry, Miss Collins, but I was
> scared and didn't have anywhere else
> to go.

MISS COLLINS

> What happened?

JACOB

> I've been getting harassed by one of
> the gang leaders over by my
> neighborhood. He put a gun to my head
> the other day. And today, he found me
> again, as Kenny and I were walking to
> school. They kidnapped Kenny.

MISS COLLINS

Oh my God, why didn't you have someone
call the police, Jacob?

JACOB

No one cares. He told them that he
would join their gang. But he did it to
save me. He really didn't wanna do it.

Miss Collins ponders in deep thought.

MISS COLLINS

I could start picking you up in the
mornings for school. You would have to
wake up a little earlier, but I don't
mind, Jacob. You're one of my best
students, and you will make it.

Jacob puts his head down in distress.

JACOB

No, that's okay, Miss Collins. I can't
let anything happen to you. It's not
safe.

(beat)

God won't let anything happen to me, I
think. I'm starting to feel like I have
a purpose in life now.

Miss Collins leans over between the seats and hugs Jacob.

MISS COLLINS

Oh, Jacob, he does, he really does
have plans for you. Come on, we must
get you home.

EXT. ALLEY -- NIGHT

Gang members crowd around. Kenny, afraid and alone, stands in the middle of the tumultuous crowd. Gino and Ja'heve sit on top of a HUMMER smoking a blunt (marijuana).

GINO

(to Ja'heve)

>   So, you say this little nigga wanna be
>   down, huh?

JA'HEVE

>   Yea, Gino, he approached me and said he
>   wanted to join.

Gino looks a bit suspicious. Ja'heve is unsuspecting.

GINO

>   Start the show, Negro.

Ja'heve hops down off the Hummer. The crowd of noisy gangsters' parts for him, like the Red Sea. Ja'heve walks up to Kenny.

JA'HEVE

>   You ready for this, Special K?

KENNY

>   I thought you said I wouldn't get
>   jumped.

JA'HEVE

>   Shut up and man up!

Ja'heve turns to face the hype crowd.

JA'HEVE (CONT'D)

Alright yawl, this here is little Kenny,
a.k.a, Special K! Tonight, this little
nigga will become a Circle.

The crowd cheers with excitement. Kenny is petrified. Starts
to HYPERVENTILATE. Ja'heve turns back to Kenny and
squats down in front of him.

JA'HEVE (CONT'D)

It's initiation time; now, just relax.
One day, you'll be a killer just like
me.

Kenny calms down a bit.

JA'HEVE (CONT'D)

Now, this is how it's gonna happen.
Four little Circles are gonna punch you
in the face as hard as they can. Then
when the fifth one approaches you if you
ain't knocked out by then, you fight'em.
You got it?

KENNY

Yea.

JA'HEVE

(facing the crowd)

Let's do it!

Five young gang members emerge from the crowd. They
form a straight line. Suddenly, the first one charges Kenny
with a clenched fist. Kenny tenses up as he prepares for
the hit... WHACK!

CUT TO:

EXT. CLASSROOM -- MORNING

Jacob waits patiently for Kenny outside of his classroom. He then starts looking eagerly up and down the hallway. Kenny comes walking around the corner.

Jacob's face lights up. He rushes towards Kenny. As he gets closer, he can see that Kenny has an ugly BLACK EYE, coupled with a bruised cheek and busted lip.

Kenny is not pleased to see Jacob.

JACOB

Kenny, what happened to you?

KENNY

What do you think happened? I got jumped in last night.

JACOB

I'm sorry, Kenny. It was supposed to be me, not you. I'll fix this somehow. You'll see, I'm gonna get you out.

KENNY

Yea, right! Don't show your face, or Ja will kill you for sure.

JACOB

I have to do something; you'll be dead in a year. Gang bangers don't live long, Kenny.

KENNY

(sadly)

I know... but there is still hope for you, Jacob.

JACOB

But, Kenny --

KENNY

I gotta go. If I'm seen talking to you, it won't be good for me.

Kenny drops his head, then hurries into the classroom.

EXT. JACOB'S LIVING ROOM -- EVENING

A rarely sober Keisha sits Indian Style on the floor. She flicks through the TV channels, scratching about her arms and neck. A PREACHER on TV ironically commands her attention.

PREACHER

Stop! Hold it right there. Put down the remote control. This is not an accident. You didn't turn to this television channel at this hour, at this second, or at this moment by chance. God!!! Led you here.

Dumfounded, Keisha sets the remote control aside. She peers deeper into the TV screen.

PREACHER (CONT'D)

This is a prophetic moment because someone watching this program is on drugs, and the devil is destroying their life and robbing their home of tranquility.

Keisha's face is seized by mixed emotions.

PREACHER (CONT'D)

The message is simple, really... Fight!
You've got to fight back. In Jesus name,
stop letting the enemy steal the gift
that God has placed inside of you. And
stop letting the devil lie to you. You
are not worthless. You are a child of
God. You're not a Junkie, you're not a
crackhead, you are loved, and you are a
child of God!

Overcome with emotion, tears stream down her face. Keisha
rolls about on the floor, crying in despair.

PREACHER (CONT'D)

My time is about up, but I can't leave
without telling you that God wants you
to be saved. If you're ready to be
saved, repeat these words after me.

Keisha sits up on her knees. She wipes her tears.

PREACHER (CONT'D)

Repeat after me: "Father, I come before
you as a sinner. I believe in your
word. I believe that Jesus Christ died
on the cross for my sins and that he
rose on the third day. I invite you
into my heart and ask that you guide my
life.

(beat)

In Jesus name, Amen."

KEISHA

(simultaneously)

"Father, I come before you as a sinner.
I believe in your word. I believe that

```
Jesus Christ died on the cross for
my sins and that he rose on the third
day.  I invite you into my heart and ask
that you guide my life.  In Jesus name,
Amen."
```

PREACHER

```
God bless you.
```

A TV commercial cuts on.

Keisha rises to her feet, crying silently.

She closes her eyes.

Keisha gracefully stretches her arms high above her head.

She twirls around slowly in a circle.

KEISHA

(whispering)

```
        Hallelujah, thank you, Father.
```

INT. BATHROOM -- CONTINUOUS

Keisha enters the bathroom. She walks over and stares intensely into the mirror.

KEISHA

(whispering)

```
        I have to change for Jacob.  I need to
        change for myself.  I must be the mother
        that God wants me to be.
```

Keisha looks at all the disturbing TRACK MARKS on her arm. She flips up her wildly tangled hair and grimaces at the sight of multiple track marks on her neck.

Keisha walks over and turns on the shower.

She walks back over to the mirror. She opens her mouth, revealing awful stained teeth. Keisha shakes her head in disgust. Finally, she notices her ghastly appearance.

She pulls out a tube of toothpaste and vigorously brushes her PLAQUE STAINED teeth.

Keisha quickly rinses her mouth with water. She opens her mouth revealing a not-so-discolored set of teeth.

Keisha looks ashamed as she removes her stained clothes. She slowly steps into the steamy shower and closes the curtain.

Loud cries ECHOES throughout the bathroom.

INT. JACOB'S BEDROOM -- MORNING

Jacob lies sound asleep. Suddenly, he awakes sniffing about.

JACOB
What's that smell? It can't be food.

Jacob climbs out of bed and tiptoes out into the HALLWAY with his nose high in the air. He looks a bit suspicious.

INT. KITCHEN -- CONTINUOUS

Jacob enters. Two plates full of delicious breakfast food sit on the table. Jacob's eyes light up with excitement.

He rushes over - stares at the food in bewilderment. Keisha enters the kitchen with a huge grin on her face. She looks vibrant for the first time in years.

KEISHA

Morning, Jacob.

JACOB

Mom! Look at you, you look beautiful.

KEISHA

Thank you, baby.

JACOB

Did you cook --

KEISHA

I was waiting to see how long it was
going to take you to wake up. Don't
stare at it, eat up, baby.

Jacob grabs a seat and eats as if the food is about to
disappear. Keisha walks over and joins Jacob for breakfast.
A serene smile brushes across her face.

JACOB

(mouth full)

Thank you, Mom.

KEISHA

No, thank you.

Keisha slides off the chair and kneels beside Jacob.

KEISHA (CONT'D)

Look at me, baby.

Jacob stops eating for a moment.

KEISHA (CONT'D)

There's going to be a lot of changes
around here. I'm sorry for walking around
here like a zombie for the past five years.
It was the drugs.

(low crying)

> Those damn drugs and my lack of will power.

Jacob hangs onto every word, as he stares deep into his mother's eyes.

KEISHA (CONT'D)

> But not anymore, I choose to live for the Lord and for you, and I know by doing that, I'll be living for myself as well.

Jacob grabs his mother and holds her tight.

JACOB

> I believe you, Mom. For the first time, I believe you.

An isolated TEAR sails down Jacob's cheek.

KEISHA

> Does this mean that you forgive me for not being here for you, Jacob?

JACOB

> I guess I do, because I'm crying.

A dumbfounded facial expression condemns Keisha's face.

JACOB (CONT'D)

> What I mean is that, I cried for so many years, especially at night when there was nothing to eat. I cried so much that I thought I would drown myself to sleep.

In a haste, Keisha pulls Jacob in close. She holds him tight, and plants a tender kiss on his forehead. A host of overwhelming mixed emotions ripples across her face.

DISSOLVE TO:

SERIES OF SHOTS:

AIDS CLINIC - Keisha sits nervously out in the lobby. A nurse greets her and reveals her test results. The result reads: HIV NEGATIVE. Keisha puts her head down between her legs. The nurse consoles her. Keisha hugs the nurse.

GROCERY STORE - Keisha grabs several boxes of cereal for Jacob and tosses them in the cart. An OLD LADY looks baffled.

DENTAL OFFICE - Keisha sits awkwardly in the dental chair. The DENTIST holds up Keisha's x-ray charts. He shakes his head in disbelief. Keisha is embarrassed and looks the other way.

INT. JOB CENTER - TWO WEEKS LATER -- MORNING

Stuck in a congested line, Keisha waits patiently to speak with an administrator. An IRATE WOMAN tries to force her way to the front of the line.

IRATE WOMAN
Yawl should get the hell out my way.

A nearby heavy-set SECURITY GUARD notices the commotion. He wobbles over and grabs the irate woman by the arm.

SECURITY GUARD

(breathing heavily)

> Now you know, you can't be cutting in line
> like this here. What's your problem, Lady?
> Huh? What the hell is wrong witcha?

IRATE WOMAN

> You better take those fat hands off me,
> before I clock you in the damn head with
> my purse, nigga.

The security guard calls for back-up on his radio.

IRATE WOMAN (CONT'D)

> Okay, I'm sorry. Damn, you can't take a
> joke. The customer service lady said
> that I could get my spot back in line.
> I had to wait two days to get my birth
> certificate.

The security guard chuckles.

SECURITY GUARD

> So, you're trying to get your place in
> line from two days ago. Damn, Lady,
> are you on crack?

Other security guards come rushing over and they both escort
the irate woman to the back of the line.

A LADY standing next to Keisha speaks out. Keisha ignores
the lady, keeping her eyes focused on the front of the line.

LADY

> Like she's the only bitch that needs
> a job. She better keep her ass back
> there.

KEENAN, well-dressed, 32, tall with a slender build, walks by. He notices Keisha standing in the crowded line. Keenan does an about-face and approaches Keisha from behind. Taps her on the shoulder.

Startled, Keisha jumps as she turns around.

KEISHA

Keenan!

KEENAN

Keisha Williams.

Keenan gives Keisha a tight hug.

KEENAN (CONT'D)

How have you been?

Keisha appears a bit nervous. She tries to hide her face with her hair.

KEISHA

Not too good, but I'm doing better now.

KEENAN

Sorry to hear that, but I'm glad you're doing better now. So, what are you do --

Keenan looks around.

KEENAN (CONT'D)

-- Forgive me, that was a stupid question that I was about to ask. Come with me, you don't have to wait in this line.

KEISHA

I can't lose my place; I've been
standing here an hour.

Keenan takes Keisha by the hand.

KEENAN

It's okay, I work here. Come on.

Keisha follows Keenan.

OFFICE

Keenan shuts the door. Many plaques and
achievement awards decorate the wall of
Keenan's elaborate office.

KEENAN

Go ahead and have a seat.

Keisha, timid and shy, hesitates to sit down.

KEENAN (CONT'D)

I won't bite, I promise.

Keisha finally sits down. Keenan takes a seat and reclines
back in his chair some.

KEENAN (CONT'D)

I still can't believe it. I'm in the
presence of Keisha Williams. You look
good. Where have you been all these
years?

KEISHA

On drugs.

A look of disbelief grips Keenan's face.

KEENAN

Drugs!

KEISHA

Yea, whoever would have thought that I would turn into a crackhead back when we were in high school?

KEENAN

Do you need to go to rehab, I'll be happy to help you if you want me to?

KEISHA

No, thank you, Keenan, but I quit two weeks ago. After I gave my life to the Lord, I just quit.

KEENAN

Wow, that's amazing.

KEISHA

Now, I'm just in need of some type of training to get a decent job.

KEENAN

Well, I'm willing to help you in any way I can. What type of training are you looking for?

KEISHA

I don't know, it's been so long since I've even thought about pursuing any type of career goals. I guess I need to rediscover what my interests are.

KEENAN

Absolutely, I understand. I will need you to complete a career assessment test

to see which career category you fall
into and go from there. It's all free,
so don't worry about money.

KEISHA

Thank you so much.

KEENAN

No problem. I'm the director of this
facility, so anything you need, I'll
make sure you get it.

Keisha is impressed. She blushes.

KEISHA

Wow, you've really made something of
yourself. I'm proud of you, Keenan.

KEENAN

Yea, me too.

Keenan laughs.

KEENAN (CONT'D)

Thank you! Say, are you dating anyone
at the moment? If not, I would love to
take you out to dinner sometime.

KEISHA

No, I don't have anyone but my son
Jacob.

KEENAN

Ahh, you got a little boy?

KEISHA

Yea, he's ten.

KEENAN

Can't wait to meet him. So, is that a
yes for dinner?

KEISHA

Sure, that sounds nice. But I'm warning
you now, I'm pretty rough around the
edges. I've been through a lot, Keenan.

KEENAN

I understand, I just want to help you,
you know. I really would like us to get
to know each other again.

KEISHA

That sounds nice.

KEENAN

Good. Well, let's get you taken care
of.

EXT. BASKETBALL COURT -- 6:00 AM

Jacob, dressed in his basketball attire, shoots some hoops at a
tainted bent rim with a tattered-torn net.

Out of nowhere comes PRUVAL, late 40s, unshaven, very
tall with a muscular build. Mysterious-looking fellow. His
decrepit shabby attire gives the impression of a homeless
person. Pruval has a liquor bottle clenched in his hand.

Pruval watches Jacob shoot-around. Jacob notices Pruval
and smiles. Pruval smiles back. Jacob shoots another shot
and misses. Then he passes the ball to Pruval.

JACOB

Shoot!

Pruval catches the ball with one hand. He sits down the
bottle. Shoots while looking at Jacob. Amazingly, he makes
the basket.

JACOB (CONT'D)

Wow, how did you do that?

Pruval doesn't reply. He walks over and hands the ball to
Jacob.

JACOB (CONT'D)

Hey, Mr., how did you do that?

PRUVAL

Faith.

JACOB

What's that?

PRUVAL

To believe without any doubt.

JACOB

Interesting. Thanks, Mr., I try to learn
a new word every day.

PRUVAL

My name is Pruval, and you are?

JACOB

Jacob.

PRUVAL

Nice name, biblical even. Nice to meet
you, Jacob.

Pruval reaches out and shakes Jacob's hand.

JACOB

Are you homeless? You look lost, like you shouldn't be around here. I mean, the way you look, you fit in. But you talk like you shouldn't be around a place like this.

Pruval smiles.

PRUVAL

Let's just say, I'm far away from home, but yet so close.

JACOB

I don't know what that means, but okay.

PRUVAL

Why are you out here so early, son?

JACOB

This is the only safe time to shoot some hoops. All the gangbangers and drug dealers are asleep this time of day. They stay up late, so they like to sleep in.

PRUVAL

Sorry, it has to be that way.

JACOB

Yea, me too, but that's life, right?

PRUVAL

You have a lot of wisdom.

JACOB

That's how God made me.

Pruval nods his head.

Jacob walks over to a bench that has been sawed in half and grabs his backpack.

JACOB (CONT'D)

It was nice meeting you Pruval. One day, you'll have to teach me that trick shot you made.

Pruval doesn't reply. He jams the liquor bottle in his jacket. Pruval smiles at Jacob, then walks off.

Jacob picks up his basketball and makes his way back home. He pulls out his notebook and writes as he takes a shortcut home.

EXT. ALLEY -- CONTINUOUS

Walking along, Jacob suddenly trips over something and falls. He sees a dead body lying next to him. He is startled. He jumps up, grabs his notebook, and runs off.

JACOB

Oh, God! Oh God! I gotta get home.

Jacob suddenly stops dead in his tracks. He turns around slowly, staring back at the dead body.

Jacob runs back over to the lifeless corpse. It's A WOMAN. Her throat is SLICED. Jacob sheds a few tears.

JACOB (CONT'D)

What sick person would do such a thing? Who would want to kill a woman?

Jacob Kneels down beside the deceased woman. He raises his BLOODY hand and removes his hat. Then he bows his head.

JACOB (CONT'D)

```
Dear God, I pray that this woman is up
in Heaven with you now.  No longer is
she trapped here in this ghetto.  She's
free.  I pray that she gets a proper
burial.  In Jesus name, A-men.
```

Jacob leans over and closes her EYES shut. He walks over by the dumpster and grabs a large piece of cardboard. Jacob then lays the cardboard over the woman, covering the upper half of her body.

INT. JACOB'S LIVING ROOM -- MOMENTS LATER

Keisha sits quietly on the floor, filling out job applications. Jacob paces slowly into the room. He's not well. Still haunted by the image of Jane Doe.

KEISHA

```
Jacob baby, where have you been so early
in the morning?
```

Jacob stands still in front of her; he doesn't reply. Keisha looks up and sees blood all over Jacob's hands. She quickly jumps up.

KEISHA (CONT'D)

```
Jacob, what happened? Are you alright?
```

INT. BATHROOM -- CONTINUOUS

Keisha nervously rushes in and quickly washes his hands off.

KEISHA

Jacob, answer me! What happened? Are
you alright?

Keisha grabs a towel and dries off his hands.

JACOB

(softly)

I'm okay. Don't worry, this is not my
blood.

KEISHA

Then whose blood is it? Jacob, what did
you do?

JACOB

Nothing! On my way home from shooting
around at the court, I took a shortcut
through the alley and tripped over a
dead body.

KEISHA

Oh my God, are you okay, baby?

JACOB

I don't know. I've seen a dead body
before, but I've never seen a dead woman
before.

KEISHA

It was a woman?

JACOB

Yea, someone sliced her throat. It
was blood everywhere. I think what
bothers me the most, is that I've always
pictured you that way.

A dubious look grips Keisha's face.

JACOB (CONT'D)

All those drugs you were doing, I thought that I would wake up, or come home from school one day, and find you in here dead, Mom.

Keisha hugs Jacob.

KEISHA

Oh, no, baby. No. God willing, nothing like that will ever happen. Don't worry, baby, I'm going to get a good job and get us out of here. We are going to move to a really nice neighborhood, or out into the suburbs somewhere.

JACOB

Okay, Mom, but if you don't, I will.

KEISHA

(smiling)

What do you mean, Jacob?

Jacob takes off his backpack and pulls out his notebook.

JACOB

This is how! I'm a writer, Mom; I think that's what God has planned for me. I was meant to write. This notebook is the story of my life, all the bad things that have happened to me and all the good, but it's mostly all bad. When I run out of pages, I'm going to send it in to a publishing company and enter the competition.

Keisha is impressed.

KEISHA

What do you know about a publishing
company, Jacob?

JACOB

Kenny actually found this and gave it
to me. Miss Collins encouraged me too.
Look, Mom.

Jacob pulls out the folded-up entry form from a backpack.
He hands it to his mom. Keisha unfolds the paper and reads.

KEISHA

"Redridge Publishing Company's First
Annual Writing Competition. Open to all
genres of fiction and non-fiction literary
works. If under eighteen years of age,
must have parents' permission to enter.
First-place winner will receive a fifty-
thousand-dollar cash prize and a book
deal." Wow! You think you can win,
baby?

JACOB

I do.

KEISHA

Well, good luck, baby, I hope you win
too. Always tell it like it is and
don't hold back anything.

Keisha hands Jacob back the enrollment form.

KEISHA (CONT'D)

Who's Miss Collins? You said she gave
you this contest --

JACOB

Uh, my teacher!

KEISHA

Oh... that's so sad. I don't even know who your teacher is. I guess I got a long way to go, huh?

JACOB

Yea, I'll say so.

(now smiling)

But you can do it, Mom. If you can quit drugs, you can do anything.

KEISHA

You're right, baby. I can. I just have to take it one step, one day, at a time.

Keisha kisses Jacob on the head.

JACOB

Hey, Mom, now that you're sober and every-thing, I want to ask you a question.

KEISHA

What is it, baby?

JACOB

Where did you get money to buy my new clothes? I mean, we wouldn't even have food in the house, but I would have new clothes --

KEISHA

(nervously)

Uh, I can't discuss that right now, baby.

Keisha appears irritated. As if she's been confined to a corner. She hurries out of the bathroom.

KEISHA (CONT'D)

Keep writing, Jacob. Keep writing, honey, and never stop.

Jacob wonders if he said something wrong. Not sure why mom reacted the way she did. He shrugs his shoulders and eases out of the bathroom.

CUT TO:

INT. JACOB'S APARTMENT - ENTRANCE -- LATER

A sweaty MAINTENANCE MAN finishes up installing new locks on the front door. Keisha is relieved.

MAINTENANCE MAN

Whoop, there it is! Ha. Ha. Ha.

The maintenance man hands Keisha a new set of keys.

KEISHA

Oh, thank you so much. Are you sure it's okay to pay you on the first of the month?

MAINTENANCE MAN

It's all good, Keisha. I'm glad to see you doing better, baby. You don't got nobody stalking you, do ya?

KEISHA

Uh, it's kind of complicated --

MAINTENANCE MAN

I understand. Well, be careful.

KEISHA

I will, thanks again.

The maintenance man heads out, and Keisha closes the door behind him.

INT. JACOB'S CLASSROOM -- DAY

Jacob sits quietly at his desk, working a math problem. The school bell SOUNDS. All the kids quickly gather their belonging and rush out. Jacob packs his books slowly into his backpack. Miss Collins walks over to check on him.

MISS COLLINS

How are you feeling, Jacob? You were pretty quiet today in class.

JACOB

Yea, I know. Just have a lot on my mind, I guess.

MISS COLLINS

Is anything bothering you, honey?

JACOB

See, that's just the thing. Nothing has really been bothering me. I'm actually happy because my mom got off drugs.

Miss Collins looks skeptical.

MISS COLLINS

Oh really!

JACOB

Yea. Can you believe it? I'd never
thought that I'd see the day. But it's
scary too. I hope she stays sober,
forever.

MISS COLLINS

I'm not so sure, Jacob. Most people
that quit drugs relapse during the first
year. Meaning that they start using
them again.

Jacob ponders in deep thought.

JACOB

Well, I'm going to stay positive and
pray.

MISS COLLINS

I just don't wanna see you get your
hopes up, and then get hurt. I've
been doing a lot of thinking and soul-
searching, Jacob. I'm going to see to
it, that you get taken care of.

JACOB

What do you mean, Miss Collins?

MISS COLLINS

You'll see, soon enough!

INT. MOVING 07' HUMMER -- DAY

Gino parks a half a block from Keisha's apartment. Music
BLASTs from the truck as he smokes a marijuana cigar. His
eyes dead-locked on Keisha's apartment.

81

CUT TO:

INT. REST ROOM -- CONTINUOUS

Keisha leans in close to the mirror. She looks beautiful. She finishes the final touches on her makeup. Gazing into the mirror, she smiles.

KEISHA

(calling out)

```
Okay, I'm ready, Jacob.  Close your eyes
and count to five.
```

JACOB (O.S.)

```
Okay!  One, two --
```

INT. LIVING ROOM -- CONTINUOUS

Keisha tiptoes into the living room. She has on a stunning black dress. Perfectly CONTOURED to her body. She is breath-taking.

JACOB

```
-- Three, four, five.
```

Jacob slowly slides his hands away from his eyes. His face lights up. He's lost for words.

KEISHA

```
Well?
```

JACOB

```
Wow!  You look amazing.
```

KEISHA

```
You really think so?
```

JACOB

Definitely.

Keisha gracefully turns about. Jacob smiles as if he never wants to forget this moment.

Suddenly, there's a KNOCK at the door.

JACOB (CONT'D)

It's showtime!

Jacob races to the door. Keisha slowly follows behind him.

DOORWAY

Jacob SWINGs the door open. Keenan recoils slightly.

KEENAN

Hey, what's up, little man? You must be Jacob.

Jacob greets Keenan with a handshake.

JACOB

Nice to meet you, sir.

KEENAN

Strong grip. I like that. Please, call me Keenan.

Keenan gives Jacob a black baseball style hat with the word "WRITER" inscribed in WHITE on the front.

JACOB

Wow!

An excited Jacob takes off his old hat and puts on the "WRITER" hat.

JACOB (CONT'D)

Thank you, Keenan!

KEENAN

You're welcome, Jacob. Your mother
told me that you like to write. So,
there you go, little man. Let your
imagination take flight.

Keisha finally reaches the door -- Keenan's mouth gapes
open. He is momentarily paralyzed by her beauty.

KEENAN (CONT'D)

(to Keisha)

And "beauty" was her name.

Keisha blushes then greets Keenan with a warm
hug. Keenan's cologne pleases her nostrils.

KEISHA

Um ..., you smell good.

KEENAN

Mr. Armani never fails.

Jacob rushes them out the door.

JACOB

Okay, my ears can't take no more. You
guys can flirt over dinner.

Keenan and Keisha laugh.

KEISHA

Okay, bye, Jacob. See you in a bit.

Jacob nods his head.

KEENAN

Nice meeting you Jacob. I wanna read
your writing sometime.

JACOB

(all smiles)

Okay! See you guys -- have fun.

EXT. APARTMENT -- CONTINUOUS

Like a perfect gentleman, Keenan escorts Keisha to his nice
Luxurious 740 BMW. Keenan opens the door for her; she
smiles with delight as she enters. Keenan shuts the door,
strolls around the backside, and hops in.

BACK TO GINO

Gino FROWNS at the sight of Keenan and Keisha together.
He takes a puff of the marijuana cigar and blows out a gust of
endless smoke. The smoke clouds his face. He sits looking
like some type of monster.

GINO

Keenan.

Gino waits for Keenan to pull off, then follows a safe distance
behind him.

INT. JACOB'S APARTMENT - BATHROOM --
CONTINUOUS

Excited, Jacob rushes into the bathroom. He looks at himself
in the mirror with his "WRITER" hat on. Jacob rubs his
finger across all the letters.

JACOB

```
Writer.  Yeah...  I'm a writer, so I got
to write.  Right!
```

Jacob turns off the light and hurries out of the bathroom.

JACOB'S BEDROOM

Jacob grabs his backpack that's slung over his bedpost and pulls out his notebook. He hops onto his bed and snatches his pen from the notebook.

Jacob slowly opens his notebook.

JACOB

```
Halfway there.
```

Jacob has filled half the pages of his notebook. He looks up at the ceiling, as he visualizes for a moment.

JACOB (CONT'D)

```
Ah, I got it.
```

JACOB WRITES:

JACOB (CONT'D)

```
"Well, it's week three and my mother
is still sober.  I know that she is
proud of me, but at the same time, I'm
very proud of her.  I thank God.  For
the longest time, my mother has walked
around here lifeless like a mummified
being, but tonight, she looked like an
Angel.  Again, I thank God."
```

INT. ITALIAN RESTAURANT -- NIGHT

Keenan pulls out Keisha's chair. Overwhelmed by this perfect gentleman, Keisha blushes as she sits down. Keenan sits down across from her.

> **KEENAN**
>
> You okay, Keisha?

> **KEISHA**
>
> Yes... it's just --

A WAITRESS approaches the table.

> **WAITRESS**
>
> Good evening. My name is Tiffany, and I'll be your server this evening. Can I start you two off with something to drink?

> **KEENAN**

(to the waitress)

> Uh, yes, we'll each have a glass of Ca'del Bosco.

The waitress pulls out her note pad and writes.

> **WAITRESS**
>
> Good choice. You two need a moment to order?

Keenan glances over at Keisha - she smiles.

> **KEENAN**
>
> Yeah, give us a few minutes. Thanks.

WAITRESS

Okay, will do. I'll be right back with
your wine.

The waitress hurries off. Keisha flips through the menu.

KEISHA

I love Italian.

KEENAN

Good. I'm glad you approve.

Keenan watches Keisha browse through the menu.

KEENAN (CONT'D)

What do you have a taste for?

KEISHA

I don't know. This "Tour of Italy"
looks good. I think I'll have that. I
love Fettuccini Alfredo.

KEENAN

Good choice, I get that every time I
come here.

KEISHA

Oh really?

KEENAN

Yeah, but I might get something else
tonight.

KEISHA

Why? It's okay if we order the same
thing.

KEENAN

Yeah, I know, but it just kind of
reminds me of when people used to dress
alike back in the early nineties.

Keisha LAUGHS.

The waitress slowly walks up with their two glasses of wine.
She carefully places them on the table.

WAITRESS

Here you are. Ready to order?

KEENAN

We'll have the "Tour of Italy."

The waitress jots it down.

WAITRESS

Okay. Coming right up.

She places some extra napkins on the table, then rushes off.
Keenan and Keisha sip their glass of wine.

EXT. ITALIAN RESTAURANT -- CONTINUOUS

Gino's Hummer slowly cruises past the restaurant.

BACK TO KEENAN AND KEISHA

KEENAN

So, how long has it been?

KEISHA

At least twelve years.

KEENAN

Yeah... Say, I'm glad you came out to dinner with me tonight.

KEISHA

I'm glad you invited me.

KEENAN

(cautiously)

Keisha, look… I gotta be straight with you. I wanna know everything that you've been through. Everything that you're comfortable telling. Your past, the drugs, everything. But at the same time, I know that it's a lot to ask. But do understand, I never stopped loving you.

Keisha is speechless; she's overwhelmed and in disbelief.

(Beat)

KEENAN (CONT'D)

So, whenever you're ready, I'm here for you and I --

KEISHA

(soft whisper)

-- I love you too.

Keenan becomes a bit emotional - his eyes water. Plays it off by pretending to have something in his eye. Suddenly, the waitress comes back with their steamy dinner.

WAITRESS

Two "Tours of Italy." Careful, it's hot.

The waitress carefully sits their plates before them.

WAITRESS (CONT'D)

Enjoy.

The waitress hurries off.

They both struggle to eat, as they stare intently at one another. They've exposed their vulnerability - now, they really don't know what to say to one another.

KEENAN

Smells good.

KEISHA

(focused on Keenan)

It does.

They both happen to take a sip of wine simultaneously.

KEISHA (CONT'D)

Well, that was quite an icebreaker, Keenan. You've left me almost speechless. I don't know what else to say, I'm --

KEENAN

Why didn't you choose me? Why Gino?

KEISHA

He said that he would kill you. And I believed him.

Keenan looks as if he's just seen a ghost.

KEENAN

Huh! Kill me.

KEISHA

When I built up enough courage to try and leave him, he shot me up with dope. Turned me into a junky.

KEENAN

(upset)

Where is he now?

KEISHA

Don't know; I've not seen him in a few weeks.

KEENAN

So, Jacob is his son, I take it?

KEISHA

Yes!

KEENAN

How often does --

KEISHA

No, Jacob doesn't know who his father is. He's never even seen Gino, before.

Keenan is confused.

KEISHA (CONT'D)

I know, it's complicated. That's why I need to hurry and move. I've already got the locks changed. As soon as I save up enough money, I'm gonna get us out of that neighborhood.

KEENAN

You and Jacob can move in with me.

KEISHA

Oh no - we couldn't impose on you like
that. Besides, we got to get to know
each other again.

KEENAN

Well, at least, let me put you two up in
an apartment uptown.

KEISHA

I appreciate the offer, Keenan, but
I have to stand on my own this time
around. I need to do this for myself
and Jacob. You understand, don't you?

KEENAN

Yeah, I do. It's just a dangerous
situation, that's all. I just don't
wanna see you hurt.

Keenan stretches his arms forth across the table and holds
Keisha's hands.

KEENAN (CONT'D)

It's gettin' late, let me getcha home.

Keisha rubs the back of Keenan's hand.

KEISHA

Okay.

EXT. APARTMENT -- LATER

Keisha stands with her back to the door - Keenan is positioned in front of her, holding her hands.

KEISHA

I really enjoyed tonight, Keenan.
Thanks for the dinner.

KEENAN

My treat, Keisha... Hey, do you remember
when you used to wear those "Juicy
Fruit" glasses back in high school?

Keenan cracks up laughing.

KEISHA

(embarrassed)

Oh, no. Why did you have to bring that
up?

(now laughing)

You went way back on that one --

Suddenly, out of nowhere, Gino approaches. He's pissed off.

GINO

(sarcastically)

Yea, I remember those damn glasses!

Keisha is petrified, but tries to remain calm. Not intimidated, Keenan cautiously moves Keisha behind him - shielding her.

KEENAN

Gino...

GINO

Yeah, nigga, it's me. What's up,
Keenan?

KEENAN

You know what's up, Gino. Just back
off. You've done enough damage already.

GINO

Nigga, is you crazy, do you know who I
am?

KEENAN

I used to.

GINO

What's that supposed to mean?

KEENAN

You know what it means, man.

GINO

I'm King of the "Circle," and I ain't
got no problem murdering that ass.

(now to Keisha)

Keisha, I told you that if I ever caught
you with Keenan, I would kill'em.

Keisha cowers behind Keenan. Gino lifts his shirt, revealing
his CHROME PISTOL HANDLE.

KEENAN

Murder me? I don't fear you, Gino, and
you know I don't. I've known you since
the first-grade, man. We used to be
best friends, man. Now, look at us.

Gino struggles to find words. He's conflicted.

GINO

You shouldn't have turned your back on me, brah.

KEENAN

What? Turn my back. I didn't turn my back on you, man. What, because you wanted to sell drugs, hustle and start a gang, and I wanted to make something of myself and go to school, to get out the hood... Nawl, Gino, you turned your back on yourself. We were never that way. Momma Toki always told us, "That just because we're stuck in the hood doesn't mean we have to be hoodlums."

Gino is wounded by Keenan's words. His eyes begin to water.

GINO

I've created too many killers to turn the tide now. I chose my path and you yours... So, I'm going to give you a free pass. This one time. Out of respect for Momma Toki. But if I catch you here again, I won't hesitate.

Gino TAPs his fingers on his CHROME PISTOL HANDLE. Keenan doesn't respond.

GINO (CONT'D)

I'll be seeing you around, Keisha.

Gino marches off and vanishes into the night.

Keenan turns about, facing Keisha - he consoles her as he gently strokes her face.

KEENAN

Keisha, let me take you away from all this. You and Jacob. Come with me.

KEISHA

No. I don't think so, Keenan. I don't want to owe you anything.

CUT TO:

INT. CLASSROOM -- DAY

The classroom is clear of children. Miss Collins sits steadfast at her desk - her cell phone pinned to her ear. The phone is RINGING. Finally, a Children Services Rep answers...

SERVICE REP

South Side Children Services Center, how can I help you?

MISS COLLINS

Yes, this is Miss Collins at Raven Elementary School and I'd like to report a case of child negligence...

SERVICE REP

Okay, what's the situation, Miss Collins?

MISS COLLINS

I have a student in my class, Jacob Kingsman, and his mother is on drugs. Well, she used to be on drugs --

SERVICE REP

Well, is she on drugs or not --

MISS COLLINS

Just let me finish, please. She's been on drugs and I guess just recently got cleaned up, but the problem is that she is very unstable and there's no telling when she is going to relapse. And my concern is for Jacob. He tells me that there is never any food in the house to eat and that he has to bum a banana from the corner store down the street from his house just to have something to eat. I've been bringing an extra lunch to school with me for him so he can have something to eat.

SERVICE REP

So, basically, the child is being starved and left home alone?

MISS COLLINS

Starved, yes. Home alone, no. The mother is always there, but she's always incoherent because she's either high or doped up on something.

SERVICE REP

That doesn't sound like an immediate emergency. You have to realize that we deal with cases where children have been beaten, raped, and molested; however, what I can do is send a case worker past the home to check things out in about a week or so.

MISS COLLINS

I understand. Well, hey, that's a start. Thank you for your time --

SERVICE REP

Wait a minute, write down your case number before you hang up. Call back next week sometime and reference this case number for a follow-up on the case.

MISS COLLINS

Okay, I'm ready.

Miss Collins grabs a pen and notebook from her desk.

CUT TO:

INT. MR. TONY'S MARKET -- MORNING

Jacob enters the store carrying a large paper sack. Mr. Tony, a large bus-built Italian, not short of 350 pounds, stands cheerfully behind the counter.

MR. TONY

Hey Jacob! How's it going?

Jacob smiles as he places the large sack on the counter.

JACOB

Just repaying my debt, Mr. Tony.

Jacob pushes the sack closer to Mr. Tony.

JACOB (CONT'D)

Well, I figure I must have eaten five weeks of bananas, one banana per day totals thirty-five. So, here you go,

Mr. Tony, seven stacks of bananas with five bananas on each, equals thirty-five bananas.

Mr. Tony is delighted. It's obvious that he's proud of Jacob.

MR. TONY

Oh, Jacob, you didn't have to repay with bananas or anything else, son.

JACOB

I know, Mr. Tony, but I figure that you lost out on seventeen dollars and fifty cents. Selling them at a rate of fifty cents per banana. In this day's economy, that's a lot of money.

MR. Tony chuckles a bit.

MR. TONY

The economy, huh? Smart kid Jacob. You got a bright future, kid.

Jacob pulls out a package from his backpack.

MR. TONY (CONT'D)

What ya got there, Jacob?

JACOB

My manuscript. I'm entering a book competition.

MR. TONY

At the age of ten and you've already written a book. You're gonna be one of the ones to make it out of this dump. I hope you win, Jacob.

JACOB

Thanks, Mr. Tony.

MR. TONY

You need me to mail that off for you?

JACOB

No, thanks, Mr. Tony. I'm gonna put it in the mail drop out front.

MR. TONY

Okay, Jacob. Keep me posted.

JACOB

I will, Mr. Tony.

EXT. SIDEWALK -- MORNING

An excited Jacob pulls out his package. The mailbox is just a short distance away. It's finally time.

JACOB

Redridge Publishing.

Jacob holds the package tight. There is no question how much this means to him.

JACOB (CONT'D)

(looking to the sky)

Well, God. Here it goes.

Suddenly, Ja'heve and few of his flunkies (gang members) walk around the corner, about 50 yards away. They spot Jacob.

JA'HEVE

Get that little nigga!

Jacob happens to look up and see them running toward him. He freezes. Looks at the mailbox. He's not sure he can make it - glances down at the package.

JACOB

```
Not now.  No!  Run, Jacob, run.
```

Jacob takes off running in the other direction. He quickly tries to place the package in his backpack. OH NO! Jacob drops the package. Ja'heve closes in. Jacob keeps running; he has no time to stop.

Jacob quickly makes a couple right turns and enters an old apartment complex. A real dump. Half of the apartments are abandoned. Boarded-up.

An old lady sitting on her porch sees that Jacob is in trouble. It's not her problem; she has too many of her own to care. She enters her house and shuts the door.

Jacob is able to force his way into one of the abandoned units.

INT. APARTMENT -- CONTINUOUS

CONDEMNED. Jacob trips over a partially burnt fire truck. Falls to the ground. Quickly crawls and hides in a corner. Jacob can hear the gang searching for him.

EXT. APARTMENT COMPLEX -- CONTINUOUS

JA'HEVE

(calling out)

```
Jacob.  Where ya at, little nigga?
Jacob!!!  I got something you want.
```

Ja'heve GRIPS the package in his hand.

BACK TO JACOB

Jacob, frantic, searches for something to use as a weapon.
He notices a 2x4 board lying across the room. He rushes
over to grab it. Jacob notices a GLOCK 23 underneath.
He's afraid to pick it up. He HEARS them getting closer.

Jacob grabs the gun and aims at the doorway. Fearing for his
life, he's ready to shoot the first person that enters.

BACK TO JA'HEVE

One of the gang members notices the door kicked in one of
the apartments. Jacob is hiding inside.

GANG MEMBER #1

Hey Ja. Look.

(pointing to the door)

JA'HEVE

Go check it out.

The gang member heads towards the apartment. Suddenly,
Ja'heve's Phone rings. He looks down at his phone. It's
Gino calling. He quickly answers.

JA'HEVE (CONT'D)

Gino. What's good?

GINO

Nothin', just looked down at my watch
and noticed you ain't where you supposed
to be.

JA'HEVE

Awl, Gino, you know, I was --

> **GINO**
>
> `-- My second in command is slippin' once`
> `again.`

Gino hangs up. CLICK!

> **JA'HEVE**
>
> `Damn!`

Right as four of the gang members are about to enter the house --

> **JA'HEVE (CONT'D)**
>
> *(now calling out)*
>
> `-- Hey ya'll, let's go.  We'll get his`
> `little ass later.`

They all quickly rush out of the apartment complex.

BACK TO JACOB

Jacob crawls over to the window. He sneaks a peek to make sure it's safe to leave. Now realizing it's safe, he breathes a sigh of relief.

Jacob places the gun back underneath the 2x4. He ponders for a moment. He quickly grabs the gun and places it in his waistband, then conceals it with his shirt.

INT. APARTMENT - JACOB'S LIVING ROOM -- EVENING

Keisha sits on the sofa filling out job applications. The phone rings. Keisha quickly answers.

> **KEISHA**
>
> `Hello.`

MS. JANICE

May I speak with Keisha Williams, please?

KEISHA

Yes. Hi, Ms. Janice, this is Keisha.

MS. JANICE

Hello dear. I just wanted to let you know that after a grueling interview process, we have decided that you're the right one for the job. Besides, you scored higher than the other applicants on the administrative test.

KEISHA

Oh, my goodness. I can't believe this. I really needed this job, Ms. Janice; you have no idea.

MS. JANICE

Oh, good for you, Keisha. You really impressed Mr. Thompson in your interview. So, can you start tomorrow?

KEISHA

Yes, ma'am. Not a problem at all, tomorrow is perfect.

MS. JANICE

Okay, Keisha, I'll see you tomorrow at nine o'clock sharp. Dress business casual.

KEISHA

Okay, thank you, Ms. Janice. Thank you so much.

Keisha hangs up the phone. So excited, she paces around for a moment, then rushes back to Jacob's room.

INT. JACOB'S BEDROOM -- CONTINUOUS

Lying across his bed, Jacob gazes out of his window at the one place that gives him comfort. The satellites blinking red light on top of the hospital off in the distance. He's in deep thought. At the same time, Jacob caresses the GLOCK 23.

Suddenly, there is a few knocks at the door. Jacob quickly places the gun underneath the pillow. Keisha enters, runs over to Jacob, hugs, and kisses him on the cheek.

KEISHA

I got the job, baby. Can you believe it?

JACOB

When can we move?

KEISHA

I don't know, baby. I'll have to save up some money first. Maybe within three months or so.

JACOB

Ok, Mom, I'm happy you got the job in all, but we got to get out of this gang-infested neighborhood soon.

KEISHA

I know, baby. We will. Is something else wrong? It looks like something is bothering you. Did you mail off your book for the contest? The deadline is in three days, right?

JACOB

Ugh, yeah. I mailed it off today.

KEISHA

Then what's up with you?

JACOB

I don't want to bother you. It's
nothing I can't handle.

Jacob glances down at his pillow.

KEISHA

What does that mean?

JACOB

Nothing, Mom, everything is fine... So,
when do you start?

KEISHA

Tomorrow, baby. I'm so excited.

JACOB

Me too, Mom. Don't worry about nothin'.
I know that you will do well.

KEISHA

Awl, thanks, Jacob. Well, let me go.
You get some rest. And I got to find
something to wear.

Keisha heads for the door --

JACOB

-- Hey, Mom. When I win that writing
contest, I'm gonna buy you a house in
the suburbs'.

KEISHA

I know you will. I love you.

JACOB

I love you too, Mom.

Keisha walks out. She's so excited.

Jacob grabs the gun and aims at a picture on his wall.

JACOB (CONT'D)

There's only one way out of this.

INT. GINO'S HOME OFFICE -- NIGHT

Dressed in a red suit including his tie, Gino sits behind his desk running stacks of CASH through a BILLCON D-551 money counter machine.

Five beautiful women help enrich his immaculate GANGSTERFIED office. Real Life poster sized photos of America's most famous gangsters occupy space on his walls.

Ja'heve enters the office. Gino doesn't look up. He instead glances down at his blinding ROLEX.

GINO

Why is my second in command late?

JA'HEVE

Gino, I --

GINO

-- This would not have nothing to do with chasin' a little ten-year-old boy around the projects, would it?

JA'HEVE

Na, Gino, I --

GINO

```
-- A boy by the name of Jacob, that
you know has my blood running through
his veins.
```

Gino gets up in Ja'heve's face. Ja'heve is nervous. Gino is the only person that strikes fear into him. The five females surround Ja'heve. Like ravenous Pitbull's ready to attack on command. They're armed with small daggers.

JA'HEVE

```
Gino. C'mon, man. Gimme a second.
You've been like a father to me. I
wouldn't harm none of your peeps,
Gino. How would that look, Gino?
```

GINO

```
Okay, Ja. But know that I will remove
yo ass like a cancerous mole if you're
lying to me.
```

The five beauties put away their daggers. They huddle around Gino. Ja'heve is relieved. He can breathe easy now.

GINO (CONT'D)

```
Let's go. We got business to attend to.
```

INT. GINO'S HOUSE - BASEMENT -- MOMENTS LATER

Four opposing GANG MEMBERS lie hog-tied on their stomachs and blindfolded on the ground.

GINO

```
Ja'heve, lift'em up.
```

Ja'heve hurries and lifts them all to their knees. The four of the beauties remove the blindfolds. They've been beaten senseless.

GINO (CONT'D)

So y'all wanna be gangsters, huh? I'll tell you what. I want y'all to run an errand for me. Go down to hell and check things out. See if there's any real gangsters down there. And when you get there, tell Lucifer I'm taking over.

They all PLEA for their life.

INT. JACOB'S APARTMENT - BATHROOM -- MORNING

Keisha finishes the final touches of her makeup. Her cell phone RINGS. She sees that it's Keenan calling and answers.

KEISHA

Morning, Keenan.

KEENAN

Morning, beautiful. Congratulations on your new job.

KEISHA

Thank you. But you made it possible, so thank you, Keenan.

KEENAN

No, baby girl, that was all you. All I did was get you the interview. It was up to you to sell yourself and you did just that.

KEISHA

Well, I guess there's a little truth to that.

KEENAN

Well, look, I'm not going to the office until later. Can I give you a ride?

KEISHA

Oh, thank you, Keenan. But I'm going to catch the El. I don't want to feel like I'm taking advantage of you. Besides, I don't want to put you out.

KEENAN

No. It's no problem at all, but I understand. So just call me on your lunch break and let me know how things are going, okay?

KEISHA

I sure will, Keenan. Thanks again for everything. Bye!

Keisha hangs up the phone.

INT. LIVING ROOM -- CONTINUOUS

Keisha grabs her coffee and purse. She pauses, making sure she hasn't forgotten anything.

Satisfied, she heads for the door. As soon as Keisha places her hand on the doorknob, the door FLIES open. It's Gino and he's pissed. Keisha desperately tries to mask her fear.

KEISHA

Gino. Whoa. What are you doing here?

Gino SLAMS the door shut.

GINO

So, I see you changed the damn locks on me.

KEISHA

How did you get in here, Gino?

Gino DANGLES a key in front of her face.

GINO

I got it from that fat fuck that changed your lock.

(beat)

So, I see you all dressed up. Where the hell you going this time of morning?

KEISHA

I got a job, Gino, please let --

GINO

-- A job. You mean to tell me you got a job. You went out and got another job, when you already got one.

KEISHA

Gino. Please, I'm going to be late.

GINO

I said you already got a job. You're my slave!!!

A frightened Keisha slowly begins to backpedal.

GINO (CONT'D)

And you will always be my slave. You understand me?

Gino pulls out a SYRINGE. Keisha knows she's in serious trouble. She appears helpless, like a whimpering dog being forced to be submissive to its master.

KEISHA

No, Gino. Please no. Don't do this.
I'm trying to be a good mother to Jacob.
Don't you want that for him? Don't you
want that? For your son?!

Gino backs Keisha into a corner.

GINO

What about being good to me?

KEISHA

I don't love you, Gino! No matter how
many drugs you pump into my veins, I
will never love you.

Infuriated, Gino SMACKS Keisha to the ground. Her coffee CRASHES to the floor. Blood trickles from her nose. Gino gets on top of her.

GINO

But you will always be my slave. You
will always be my junkie.

KEISHA

(crying)

God, please! God, please don't let him
do this to me.

Gino jams the syringe into her neck and injects her with heroin.

KEISHA (CONT'D)

(whispering)

    I love you, Jacob.

Immediately, Keisha goes into convulsions and passes out. Gino leaves the syringe dangling in her neck.

GINO

    Sweet dreams, baby girl. Sleep tight.

Gino looks passionately upon Keisha. But this is not love. He's a monster. He rubs his fingers through her hair and kisses her on the lips.

Gino slowly rises up and walks off.

INT. MISS COLLINS' CLASS

The school bell RINGs. Miss Collins notices Jacob is missing among the other students.

She opens the door and looks around for Jacob. Where could he be? Miss Collins is worried.

EXT. JACOB'S APARTMENT -- LATER

A black Honda Sedan drives up followed by a police cruiser. A well-dressed woman exits the sedan. She's accompanied by two policemen. They walk up to Jacob's apartment door.

The woman gives a few loud KNOCKs at the door.

WOMAN

    Ms. Williams! This is Sharon from
    Children's Services. Open up, please.

No response... Sharon knocks a few more times.

SHARON

Ms. Williams! --

-- The door creaks open a bit. It was open the whole time. The policemen are alarmed.

POLICEMEN # 1

(to Sharon)

Step back, ma'am.

Sharon moves aside. Both officers pull out their pistols. One of the officers pushes the door open. They quickly move in with guns drawn.

INT. LIVING ROOM -- CONTINUOUS

They see Keisha lying on the floor unconscious. One of the officers quickly calls it in over the radio.

POLICEMEN # 1

Dispatch. We got a D.O.A. I mean a deceased black female. Appears to be in her early --

SHARON

-- You don't know that; you didn't even check her pulse.

Sharon rushes and checks her pulse. Nothing. She presses her ear against Keisha's chest.

SHARON (CONT'D)

She has a faint heartbeat. Hurry up and call the paramedics.

POLICEMEN # 1

Dispatch, apparently, the female has a

115

faint heartbeat. We're gonna need an
ambulance right away, please.

SHARON

I know this is the ghetto, but give life
a chance...

Police Officer # 2 reaches to grab the syringe from Keisha's neck.

SHARON (CONT'D)

No. Don't touch that. That's potential
evidence. Look at the scene. It's
possible that this could be a break-in,
or even attempted murder.

Both officers are dumfounded. Lost for words. They know she's right.

EXT. JACOB'S APARTMENT -- CONTINUOUS

Jacob sees that the door is open and rushes into the apartment.

INT. LIVING ROOM -- CONTINUOUS

JACOB (O.S.)

Mom! Momma!

Jacob runs in and sees his mother lying on the floor.

JACOB (CONT'D)

Mom!!!

Sharon tries to console Jacob.

SHARON

It's okay, son. Everything --

Jacob breaks away and runs over to his mother.

Suddenly, Keenan enters the living room. The two officers quickly apprehend him.

KEENAN

What happened? What's going on here?

SHARON

Who are you?

KEENAN

I'm a friend. My name's Keenan. I'm the director of the job center downtown. What happened?

The officers let him go. Keenan sees Keisha lying on the floor. Paramedics quickly rush in and go to work on Keisha.

SHARON

Apparently, a drug overdose. But I don't believe it was self-inflicted.

KEENAN

It couldn't have been. I just spoke with Keisha this morning. She was on her way to work.

SHARON

She does look fairly dressed. It looks like a struggle took place and she dropped her coffee perhaps.

KEENAN

(whispering)

Damn you, Gino.

POLICEMEN # 1

What was that?

KEENAN

Nothin'.

(to Jacob)

Are you okay, son? You okay, Jacob?

Jacob doesn't respond. Keenan walks over to Jacob and lifts him up.

PARMEDIC # 1

(addressing everyone)

Her pulse is very faint. We gave her a Narcan shot which should block most of the aftershock from the heroin by binding to her opioid receptors. She should make a full recovery. We have to hurry up and get her to the ER though.

KEENAN

Thank you.

The paramedics roll Keisha out on a stretcher.

EXT. APARTMENT - PORCH -- CONTINUOUS

Keenan and Jacob stand about. Sharon and police officers are in a discussion several feet away.

JACOB

Why would she do this to me again?

KEENAN

This was not her fault, Jacob.

BACK TO SHARON

SHARON

Well, I guess that's it for here.

POLICEMEN # 1

What about the kid?

SHARON

He's in the care of Children
Services for now...

Sharon glances over at Jacob. Jacob knows. He slowly backpedals and takes off.

KEENAN

Jacob!

Keenan runs after Jacob. He slips and falls. Jacob gets away.

KEENAN (CONT'D)

Damn!

SHARON

(at the officers)

Do something. Find him, he has nowhere
to go.

POLICEMEN # 1

Ma'am, we're sure he'll turn up
somewhere. He looks like a resourceful
kid.

SHARON

You're joking, right? You two are
worthless. Hopefully, he doesn't turn
up in a body bag.

The officers ignore her comment.

POLICEMEN # 1

```
Well, I'm hungry, let's get some chow.
```

EXT. CRACK HOUSE -- NIGHT

Ja'heve is on the porch - smoking a blunt. Jacob sneaks up on Ja'heve, gun DRAWN.

JACOB

```
I want you to let Kenny go, and I want
my package back.
```

JA'HEVE

```
What the hell!  If it ain't little
bitch ass, Jacob.
```

(now laughing)

```
Where you get that gun from?
```

JACOB

```
I don't want to shoot you.  But I will.
Where's Kenny and my package?  I want
them both.  Now!
```

Ja'heve sees a gang member sneaking up behind Jacob. He smiles, then takes a quick puff of the blunt and blows the smoke in Jacob's face.

JA'HEVE

```
You ain't gettin' shit.
```

Suddenly, the gang member grabs the gun from Jacob and pushes him over to Ja'heve. Ja'heve backhands Jacob in the face, pulls his gun, and presses it his face.

JA'HEVE (CONT'D)
You ready to die?

Jacob doesn't respond - he's frightened and doesn't know what to do. Ja'heve COCKS the pistol back.

JA'HEVE (CONT'D)
Better yet, I'm goin' to do you even better, little nigga.

(to the gang member)
Take his ass round back.

The gang member grabs Jacob and forces him to the back of the house.

BACK OF CRACK HOUSE

Dark alley lined with oversized filthy dumpsters and trash. Ja'heve comes out of the house with Kenny and the package.

JA'HEVE (CONT'D)
Here's your last look at Kenny and your damn package... What's in this damn package anyway?

Ja'heve reads the package. He becomes furious.

JA'HEVE (CONT'D)
Redridge Publishing Company.

(now laughing)
You really think you smart, huh? You think you gonna win this fuckin' writing competition and buy yo crackhead momma a house?

Outraged! Jacob wants to do something, but can't. He glances at the pistol gripped in Ja'heve's hand. Kenny makes eye contact with Jacob. He secretly shakes his head signaling Jacob to stand down.

JA'HEVE (CONT'D)

-- Little nigga, you ain't bigger than this.

(pointing about)

You ain't bigger than the hood, nigga... And you ain't bigger than the motherfuckin' circle. You live in the hood, you gonna die in the hood.

JACOB

Why do I have to die here? I know where I'm from. This place is like a big garbage can. Who would want to stay here, unless you're garbage? Maybe you like that smell. But I don't.

Now he's pissed off Ja'heve for the last time.

JA'HEVE

What you just say. You said I smell like shit?

JACOB

No, I didn't say that.

KENNY

No, Ja'heve, he --

JA'HEVE

-- Shut yo ass up, Kenny...

(now to Jacob)

> It's too bad you ain't gonna be able
> to enter that writing competition.
> Corpses can't talk, read, or write. And
> they sure in the hell can't mail off
> packages.

Ja'heve reaches in the back of his waistband, pulls a 22 PISTOL, and hands it to Kenny.

KENNY

> What's this for?

JA'HEVE

> What do you think? It's time to show
> your balls. Prove yourself. Murk this
> fool.

Petrified! Kenny's hand shakes uncontrollably. The gun hanging by his side.

KENNY

> But he's my best friend. I can't kill
> Jacob. He's like my --

JA'HEVE

> -- Kill Jacob, or I'm gonna kill you.

Ja'heve TARGETS Kenny with his pistol. The gang member smiles in delight. Jacob is scared shitless. He doesn't want to die. Jacob fears for Kenny as well.

JACOB

> I know you don't wanna shoot me,
> Kenny, but I don't want you to die
> either. Do what you gotta do. I'll
> see you in heaven.

Ja'heve is surprisingly touched by Jacob's words. He quickly tries to cover his feelings of remorse. He reignites his inner demon. The killer inside. Kenny starts to cry.

JA'HEVE

Shut the hell up and smoke him.

Confused. Kenny's heart POUNDS... FASTER and FASTER. He doesn't want to kill Jacob. Kenny slowly walks towards Jacob with the gun still at his side.

Jacob drops to his knees, bows his head, and begins to pray. Pruval can be seen in the distance watching; no one notices him.

JA'HEVE (CONT'D)

Watch this fool prayin'. You think God is gonna save you. God ain't gonna save yo ass. How we even know God is real? Everybody prayin' and shit. Even my own momma always prayin' and her prayers always go unanswered. Hell, I'm living proof.

CUT TO:

EXT. OUT FRONT OF CRACK HOUSE

GINO rolls up in his BLING-BLING Escalade. He quickly steps out with his gangster kitties at his side.

BACK TO JACOB

Jacob still on his knees - head down. Kenny stands before him and slowly raises the pistol to Jacob's head. Ja'heve and his gang goony smile.

JACOB'S GHETTO

Suddenly, Kenny quickly points the gun at Ja'heve, but
before he can pull the trigger, Ja'heve shoots him in the chest.
Kenny falls down beside Jacob.

JACOB

Kenny!!! No. NO. NO. No, God. No.
Not Kenny.

Jacob holds Kenny tight as he rocks him back and forth.
Kenny coughs up a bunch of blood.

KENNY

(smiling)

You knew I wasn't gonna shoot you.
Right?

JACOB

Don't die, Kenny! Please don't die!

KENNY

You knew, right?

JACOB

Yea. I knew.

Smiling, Kenny's eyes close for the last time. Jacob cries out
in agony and pain.

JA'HEVE

Sorry for your loss, little homie.

Ja'heve points his pistol at Jacob's head.

JA'HEVE (CONT'D)

Go ahead and pray again. Let see if it
works this time.

Jacob bows his head. Ja'heve slowly pulls the trigger. The gun jams. Ja'heve, in disbelief, quickly tries to get the gun unjammed. Suddenly, a loud gun blast RINGS out. Ja'heve is shot and falls to the ground. Gino stands over him.

GINO

Look at what you made me do, Ja. I told you, man. I told you. Not to mess with Jacob. How could you try and kill my son, man?

Jacob looks up in disbelief. He's confused.

JA'HEVE

You don't get it, do you? You loved your son so much that you protected him from this street life. But you inducted me in and turned me into a killer. When I realized what you had done, I hated you for that. Killing Jacob was my way of paying you back.

GINO

That what's up. You were already tainted, so I brought you in full throttle. Showed you the ropes and made you my second in command. And this is how you repay me? Say goodnight, nigga.

Ja'heve throws up the CIRCLE symbol. Jacob slowly gets up. Another large gun blast rings out. Gino finishes off Ja'heve.

GINO (CONT'D)

(to gang member)

Now you know this is my son. Don't fuck wit'em.

GANG MEMBER

Hey, whatever you say, Gino.

Gino walks over to Jacob.

GINO

Sorry about your friend. You okay, son?

Jacob rises to his feet.

JACOB

Son... I'm not your son. It all makes
sense now. That's how you knew my name.
Now I know where my new clothes came
from, but I would have rather had some
food in my belly. How come you never
came around?

GINO

I was ashamed, Jacob. Ashamed of what I
had become... A monster. You're better
off not knowing me. But I always loved
you, son, and looked out for you.

JACOB

What about my mom? You don't love me;
if you did, you wouldn't have pumped my
mother with all those drugs.

GINO

Look, Jacob. Some things you just don't
understand. But I do love you. Come
on, let's get you cleaned up.

Confounded with mixed emotions, Jacob runs off.

GINO (CONT'D)

```
Jacob, wait!
```

Jacob doesn't stop. He disappears into the darkness. Gino notices Jacob's package on the ground and picks it up.

INT. REDRIDGE PUBLISHING COMPANY - OFFICE - TWO WEEKS LATER

JACK TRENT, senior literary agent, mid 40s, shuffles through the last of the contest entries, sipping his coffee, then comes across the last package. He quickly opens the package and pulls out the notebook inside. It reads: Jacob's Ghetto.

JACK

```
Jacob's Ghetto.  Hmm.  Unusual submission
choice of format but a catchy title.
```

Jack begins to read. He's drawn in right away. Unable to put the notebook down.

JACK (CONT'D)

(reading)

```
"If I could cry for my mother, I
would.  But I cannot.  My jar of tears
for her is empty.  But who cries for
me, innocent Jacob?  I'm the only one
who cries for myself.  I'm sorry for
myself."
```

A tear trickles from Jack's eye. He's surprised. Then, he looks around the room, making sure no one saw him. He realizes he's the only one in the room, then chuckles to himself.

JACK (CONT'D)

Wow. I haven't cried in ten years.

Jack calls his assistant on the speaker phone. SARA answers.

SARA (O.S.)

Yes, Jack.

JACK

Sara. I need to see you right away.

SARA

Okay, Jack. I'll be right there.

Jack hangs up. There's a knock at the door.

JACK

Come on in.

Sara enters.

SARA

You rang?

JACK

I think I may have found our winner.

Jack hands Sara the notebook.

SARA

Really?

JACK

Yes. I love this story, Jacob's story.
He's a young talented African American
boy that lives in a gang-infested
territory who's determined to make it
out as a writer. And without having any
sympathy for the kid - he can actually

write. He's brilliant. And his vocabulary is that of a college student. Very impressive.

SARA

I see.

JACK

His story is going to change the mindset of young kids across the country.

SARA

I can't wait to read it. I haven't seen you this enthused in a long time.

JACK

Well, I haven't been inspired in a long time... Whatever you were working on, put it on hold and type this up for me. After that, send it off to the editing department right away.

SARA

Right away.

(now reading)

Jacob's Ghetto. I like the title. Okay. I'm on it.

JACK

Thanks, Sara. We got to hurry up and contact this kid. I don't want nothing to happen to him.

SARA

Yes, sir.

CUT TO:

EXT. JACOB'S APARTMENT - ENTRANCE -- DAY

Jacob and Miss. Collins walks out carrying a couple of bags and a box full of Jacob's books.

MISS COLLINS

You got everything.

JACOB

Yea. I think so.

They both walk down to the car. As they load the car, a mailman approaches Miss Collins.

MAILMAN

Here you are, Miss Williams.

The mailman hands Miss Collins some mail.

MISS COLLINS

Oh. Um, thank you.

MAILMAN

Good day.

The mailman walks along.

INT. CAR -- CONTINUOUS

Miss Collins places the mail on the back seat. She and Jacob put on their seatbelts.

MISS COLLINS

You ready for this?

With a subtle gesture, Jacob nods his head. Miss Collins drives off.

EXT. DRUG REHAB CENTER -- LATER

Miss Collins drives up and parks the car.

INT. CAR -- CONTINUOUS

MISS COLLINS

Go ahead, honey. I'll catch up.

JACOB

Ok.

Jacob exits the car. Miss Collins grabs the mail and her purse from the back seat.

INT. REHAB CENTER -- CONTINUOUS

Jacob walks slowly down the hallway with his head down. Disheveled and scared in so many ways emotionally. He doesn't want to make contact with anyone, not even himself.

INT. RECOVERY ROOM -- CONTINUOUS

Keisha finishes off a few bites of her applesauce. She picks up a hand mirror and stares intently at her reflection. She feels much better, the effects of the drugs wore off, but still there's an underlying fear buried deep inside her that pains her soul. She cracks a smile, followed by a few tears. Suddenly, there's a knock at the door.

JACOB (O.S.)

Mom!

Keisha hurries and wipes her tears and puts on a fake smile for her Jacob.

KEISHA

```
Come in, honey!
```

Jacob slowly opens the door. He's not sure what state his mother is in. She sounds and looks herself, but the uncertainly is crippling. After all, he was just nearly killed himself. As Jacob pushes the door open all the way and sees his mother in good spirits, his eyes light up with pure joy. Stuck in his tracks as if it's his first time seeing winter snow fall from the sky.

KEISHA (CONT'D)

```
Well, come here and give Momma a hug!
```

Jacob rushes over and hugs his mom tight he surprises himself. She's caught off guard too. She can feel his pain and kisses his forehead.

KEISHA (CONT'D)

```
Everything is going to be okay, baby.
```

Jacob starts sobbing uncontrollably.

KEISHA (CONT'D)

```
What's wrong, Jacob?  I'm okay, I'm
going be all right son, I'm feeling a
lot better.
```

Keisha lifts Jacob's head up.

JACOB

```
I know, Mom, you look good.
```

KEISHA

```
Then what's wrong?
```

JACOB

I almost died yesterday.

KEISHA

What?!

JACOB

Ja'heve with this gang called the Circle
has been harassing me, and he tried to
force Kenny to shoot me. But Kenny
wouldn't do it and tried to shoot him
instead. Mom... Kenny's dead, he died
for me. He died trying to save me.

Jacob breaks down again. Keisha consoles him.

KEISHA

Oh, I'm so sorry, Jacob, I know you
loved Kenny like a little brother.

JACOB

I did. Mom, I have to tell you
something else... I lied to you and I'm
sorry.

KEISHA

Lied about what?

JACOB

About entering the writing contest. I
never got a chance to mail it off. I
dropped my package when I got chased
by the gang the other day. I never
got a chance to mail it off.

Jacob looks hopeless as he pours out his heart.

JACOB (CONT'D)

No, it's not okay, Mom. I really hoped
I'd win and be able to move us out of
the ghetto.

There's a light knock at the door.

KEISHA

Come in!

Miss Collins enters the room and notices Jacob has been
crying.

KEISHA (CONT'D)

Oh, you must have the wrong room.

JACOB

No, this is my teacher, Miss Collins.

Miss Collins greets Keisha with a soft handshake.

KEISHA

Oh, it's nice to finally meet you.

MISS COLLINS

Likewise! I heard about what happened
and I'm so sorry for misjudging. I'm
the one that had Children Services go to
the home.

KEISHA

No... I'm glad you did. I'm not sure
if I would be here or not if you hadn't.
Thank you!

MISS COLLINS

I'm just glad you're feeling better...
oh, here's your mail.

Miss Collins looks over at Jacob for a moment as her face lights up.

MISS COLLINS (CONT'D)

So, Jacob, did you tell your mom all about the writing contest.

Miss Collins notices the disarray on their faces. Keisha looks at Jacob. Jacob looks up at Miss Collins.

JACOB

I didn't enter the contest. I lost my package when I got chased by the gang.

Jacob balls up his fist in anger.

JACOB (CONT'D)

I was so close too.

Miss Collins is confused.

MISS COLLINS

That's strange, then what's this?

Miss Collins reaches in her purse and hands Jacob a package. Jacob stares endlessly at the package. It reads: Redridge Publishing Company. Jacob's eyes beam with new life. He quickly rips open the package.

JACOB

(excited)

It's from Redridge Publishing Company.

(now reading)

"Dear Jacob, thank you for entering the 10th Annual Redridge Publishing Writing Competition. We're happy to announce that you are a top finalist.

The winner will be selected in two
weeks."

KEISHA

That's amazing, baby, congratulations!
My baby can write!

Keisha hugs Jacob and kisses him on the cheek. Miss Collins
joins in on the hug party.

MISS COLLINS

Awesome job, Jacob, I hope you win.

Jacob is all smiles, and yet he's confused, as he knows he
didn't send off the package.

KEISHA

Jacob, I thought you said you didn't get
a chance to enter.

JACOB

I didn't, Mom. Someone must have found
it and mailed it off for me.

FLASHBACK - GINO'S OFFICE

Gino holds Jacob's package in his hands. He sees Jacob's
name and the publishing company name on the package.
He's confused and intrigued at the same time. He pulls a
blade from the desk and opens the package. Slowly, he pulls
out the notebook.

GINO

Jacob's Ghetto!

Gino quickly opens the notebook and reads.

GINO (CONT'D)

(reading)

> "Born in what many privileged people
> would call a city of ashes, poverty,
> drug-infested, gang-scum, and poor
> people, I've always felt like a prince.
> Although my kingdom is a roach-infested,
> should-be-condemned two-bedroom
> apartment at the moment, I believe God
> has better things in store for me. Hope
> is all I have, and I pray that it's
> enough to keep me alive.
>
> Hello, I'm Jacob and please don't hold
> your breath as you journey into my
> story, Jacob's Ghetto."

In disbelief, a few tears trickle down Gino's face.

GINO (CONT'D)

> Damn, this is some powerful shit, my
> little man can write. He takes after me
> and doesn't even know it.

Gino is proud, knowing the good parts of him were passed on.

FLASHBCACK - GINO'S KITCHEN

A young 13-year-old Gino sits at the table, writing a poem.
His dad enters the kitchen, drinking a bottle of cheap liquor,
"Irish Rose."

GINO'S DAD

> What the hell you doing, boy, what you
> writing?

Gino's dad snatches the notepad from Gino.

GINO

Huh, a rap, I'm writing a rap song, Dad.

GINO'S DAD

(reading)

"When I see you, I see the summer bees,
with the warm summer breeze, your warm
smile makes me weak in my knees, girl
please, choose me." What the hell is
this bull, boy? This ain't no rap,
if it is, it's a faggot ass rap song.
Writing ain't going to save your ass in
these streets.

He rips up the poem, reaches behind his back, and pulls a gun from underneath his shirt.

GINO'S DAD (CONT'D)

You better learn how to make this Glock
talk; you understand me, boy?

Gino nods his head in fear.

END FLASHBACK - BACK TO GINO

Staring intently at Jacob's notebook, Gino realizes how he was tainted. An anger that he's hidden for so many years. Gino wipes his tears. A smile overcomes his pain. He quickly places the notebook back inside the package and walks out.

END FLASHBACK

INT. REDRIDGE PUBLISHING CO. - BOARD ROOM -- MORNING

The company's big wigs, Jack, and several other top agents fill the room. Plenty of coffee and a variety of pastries cover the center of the gorgeous oakwood oval table. Everyone is chatting amongst themselves as they eat and drink. JIM the Publisher, early 60s, starts to speak.

> **JIM**
> All right, everyone, it's decision-making time. It's time to decide our winner of the fifty-thousand-dollar, cash prize.

Jim takes a quick sip of coffee, as he looks over his clipboard, which has the title of the top five finalists and the synopsis. He grabs his reading glasses from his top pocket and put them on. He looks over the list again. His assistant tries to hand him an iPad with all the info in large fonts, but he politely declines.

> **JIM (CONT'D)**
> You know I'm old-school.

A few chuckles can be heard around the room.

> **JIM (CONT'D)**
> Ok, let's see here, our top five finalists are, The Sound of Noise, The True Keto Diet, Dark Masses, Man's Best Friend Named Sam, Cursed of Ancient Aliens and Jacob's Ghetto.

Jack smiles to himself.

JIM (CONT'D)

Now I must say that I've read most of
all of these books and I'm pleased with
what our top agents have picked as their
top choice if you will. However, we do
need a bestseller this coming year and
I do feel that Jacob's Ghetto is not a
book that can take us there.

Jack is obviously frustrated by Jim's remarks. Two of the
other agents, Steve and John, simultaneously look at each
other with a cynical grin. They know their book choice is one
step closer.

JACK

Seriously, Jim?

JIM

My pardon?

JACK

I've personally read all five books
and I must say they're all generic in
premise, plot, and overall storytelling.
How many times has there been a book
about dieting, a dog, or Aliens and
the undead? You founded this company
on originality, Jim... Jacob's Ghetto,
will be the talk of the town across
this nation. And with our marketing
campaign, it will be a new bestseller,
hands down.

Steve raises his hand.

JACK (CONT'D)

You don't have to raise your hand,

Steve, just speak.

Jim takes off his glasses and ponders in thought.

STEVE

Well, I don't wanna come off racist, but...

JACK

But, what, Steve? Go ahead and spit out your racist sly remark.

STEVE

Well, I was just gonna say, how many times has there been a Boyz N' Da Hood story? I mean, that's been done plenty of times before, right? West Side!

Steve makes an awful attempt at throwing up a gang sign. A few people laugh.

JACK

Did you even get past the synopsis, Steve?

STEVE

No.

JOHN

I did and it was sort of touching until I fell asleep. I mean, we all know that black people don't do a lot of reading, so... that right there would put a damper on sales, as I don't believe this story would do well in the white demographic. And, I'm not being racist; I'm just stating an obvious fact.

Jim puts his glasses back on, as he takes a sip of coffee and bites out of his English muffin.

JIM

I love a spirited debate, I do. But that doesn't make us money. Does anyone else have any witty comments they would like to add?

No one says a word.

JIM (CONT'D)

Jack, sell me, why Jacob's Ghetto?

JACK

Did you read the story, Jim?

JIM

I did, and I even shed a tear. I must say the story did fire up the old symphony of emotion buried deep in my old cold heart, but that's not what drives sales, Jack. As a top agent, you know that better than anyone... I believe you're too attached to some kid, birthed in a very unfortunate situation that you don't even know Jack. You don't owe this kid anything. Besides, John is right, black folks don't read much... now, they love their music, but not big on reading.

JACK

You're right. I am attached, like every other good story I've come across in my career, but this is so different and so much better than anything I've pitched you to date. You're all forgetting that

143

> emotions drive sales and this book is so touching, that it will inspire millions.

Jim is perplexed momentarily, then finally makes a decision. He takes his pen and crosses out Jacob's Ghetto from his list.

JIM

> Ok, that leaves us with four titles, pitch me!

JACK

> So, are you eliminating Jacob's Ghetto from the competition?

JIM

> Affirmative!

Jack packs up his things.

JACK

> Well, it's affirmative that I quit!

Everyone gasps in disbelief.

JIM

> Are you serious, Jack? Just because your pick didn't win.

JACK

> Suddenly, I just had an epiphany. Thanks for the opportunity, Jim; it's been a pleasure, up until now.

Jack quickly walks out of the board room.

INT. APARTMENT - JACOB'S LIVING ROOM -- A FEW WEEKS LATER

Keenan and Keisha are boxing up some of the items in the living room. Keisha blushes as she notices Keenan watching her pack. She looks back over her shoulder at him and smiles. Keenan walks over and gives Keisha a warm hug and kiss on the cheek.

KEENAN

I'm sorry, but I noticed your beautiful self from across the room and I couldn't resist the urge, you know, to come over here and talk to you.

KEISHA

Well, that's fine, but you're a little too touchy-feely and I may have to call security.

KEENAN

But I'm security.

They both laugh. Keisha takes Keenan by the hand and sits down on the couch. Keisha's whole demeanor changes as fear starts to set in.

KEENAN (CONT'D)

What's wrong, love?

KEISHA

I really don't want to be a burden to you. I really appreciate you letting us move in, but I'm not comfortable. I mean, what if things don't work out, or you change your mind about us?

KEENAN

```
Whoa!  Hey now, I've only been waiting
for fifteen years and I haven't changed
my mind yet?
```

Keisha rests her head on Keenan's chest.

KEENAN (CONT'D)

```
Everything is going to be okay.  Trust
me.
```

There are a few loud knocks at the door. Keisha looks startled; she's frightened it's Gino.

INT. JACOB'S BEDROOM -- CONTINUOUS

Jacob lies on his back in his bed with his hands folded, resting behind his head. He stares at the ceiling in deep thought. It's hard to tell what's on his mind, if anything at all. Suddenly, he takes a deep breath and rubs his eyes.

JACOB

```
So close, God... well, at least, I made
it as a finalist.  But I was really
hoping to win.  Aww, I wanted to win so
bad for my mom.
```

BACK TO KEISHA AND KEENAN

KEENAN

```
I'll get it.  Don't worry.
```

KEISHA

```
No, it's ok, I'll get it.
```

KEENAN

```
Let's go together.  Sounds like a plan.
```

KEISHA

Sure!

INT. DOORWAY -- CONTINUOUS

Keisha slowly opens the door. She's shocked to see two people, other than black, standing on her porch. It's Jack and Sara dressed in their professional business attire. Jack is carrying a briefcase. Keisha looks confused. "What could be wrong?" she thinks.

KEISHA

Yes, how can I help you two detectives?

Jack and Sara sort of look at one another.

JACK

Oh no, we're not law enforcement. I'm a publisher and literary agent, and this is my assistant Sara. May we come in and speak with you for a moment, please?

Keenan and Keisha are completely surprised.

KEISHA

Uh, yeah, sure, come on in.

Sara enters first and Jack follows behind her.

INT. KITCHEN -- CONTINUOUS

They both follow Keisha and Keenan into the kitchen.

KEISHA

Please have a seat.

Everyone quickly sits down at the table.

KEISHA (CONT'D)

So, you're with Redridge Publishing Company, I assume? Jacob just received a letter last week that he didn't win the competition.

JACK

I used to be until about three weeks ago. I'm the former agent that selected Jacob's manuscript, but the publisher and everyone else pretty much voted it down.

BACK TO JACOB

Jacob hears unusual chatter. He quickly gets up and tiptoes into the hallway.

BACK TO KEISHA

KEISHA

Oh really, wow, well, we really appreciate that. Jacob was so excited.

KEENAN

Yes, he was.

KEISHA

So, what brings you here?

JACK

Well, after Jacob's book was not selected, I was very contrite and angry, so I quit and started my own publishing company. Look, let me be as frank as I can, I left because of Jacob, and I believe his story needs to be told.

Sara picks up Jack's briefcase and pulls out a few documents.

JACK (CONT'D)

I would love for Jacob to be my very
first client and I'm offering him a
fifty-thousand-dollar sign-on bonus. I
believe in my heart that if it weren't
for certain biases, Jacob would have
won the competition.

Jack slides over the check and contract to Keisha. Keisha and
Keenan are speechless. Keisha picks up the check and takes a
close look. She's in disbelief.

KEISHA

Oh wow, I don't know what to say.

A tear trickles from Keisha's eye onto the check. Keisha
quickly tries to dry it off and blows on the check.

JACK

(smiling)

It's ok, we can always cut another check
if we need to.

Keisha laughs.

KEISHA

So, my Jacob can really write, huh?

JACK

Yes!

SARA

To be a ten-year-old boy, yes,
definitely. He has a way with words

that can't be taught. You can teach
storytelling and structure, but without
imagination and creativity, it will be
just another well-written dull story.

JACK

You never read Jacob's Ghetto,
Keisha?

KEISHA

No, Jacob is so secretive with his
writing. He never let me. He told me
what it was about, but I never read it.
I guess he wanted to surprise me.

KEENAN

So what else are you offering with this
book deal? I mean, fifty "K" is a lot
of money, but what type of book launch
and distribution are we looking at here?

JACK

The full monty, Keenan. With my
connections and expertise, I'm
talking about a national book tour,
TV interviews, etc. I believe this
story, even though a sad one, has a
very powerful message that will change
the mindsets of kids and young adults
everywhere.

Keisha is overwhelmed and breaks down. Keenan consoles her.
Jack and Sara become a bit emotional and shed a few tears.

KEISHA

(laughing)

I guess we need to call Jacob in here.

JACK

Oh, I can't wait to meet --

Suddenly, without warning, Jacob rushes in and gives Jack a huge hug.

JACK (CONT'D)

Jacob!

Jacob shakes Jack's hand.

JACOB

It's nice to meet you, Jack.

JACK

It's an honor to meet you, Jacob! I feel like I know you already. Now, I can put the face behind your amazing story.

Jacob shakes Sara's hand. Sara then gives Jacob a soft hug.

SARA

It's nice to meet you, Jacob.

JACOB

You too, Sara, it's nice to meet you as well! So, Jack, what's the name of your publishing company?

JACK

Burgeon! Do you know what --

JACOB

To grow and flourish!

Jack is impressed, but not surprised at all. He knows Jacob is special. Keisha quickly grabs and hugs Jacob.

KEISHA

Look, baby!

Keisha shows Jacob the check. Jacob is delighted; this is, by far, the happiest day of his life. Keenan bumps fists with Jacob, then hugs him.

KEENAN

I'm proud of you, Jacob.

Jack goes over the contract with Keisha and Keenan, and they all agree. Jack hands Keisha a pen, she has Jacob print his name, and then she signs the contract.

EXT. APARTMENT - PORCH - DAYS LATER

Keisha stands on the porch as she is watching Jacob and Keenan put boxes into his car. Then the mail man comes over and hands her a large package. Keisha sits down and quickly tears open the package. A few copies of Jacob's book are inside. Keisha pulls out a copy and gently rubs her hand over the cover. The cover is a life-like illustration of Jacob sitting on the sidewalk in front of their apartment building. Keisha's so overjoyed.

KEISHA

Thank you, Jesus!

Jacob rushes up to the porch.

JACOB

Cool, Mom, my book is finally here!

Jacob is so excited; he quickly flicks through the book and finds his picture at the end.

JACOB (CONT'D)

Look at me, it's me!

Keisha just continues to smile. Keenan walks up and shares the moment of happiness and joy with them.

KEENAN

This is so awesome, Jacob! Jack kept his word; this is awesome quality and the cover is amazing.

KEISHA

It is. It really is!

JACOB

Oh, Mom, could I run a copy down to Mr. Tony really quick?

KEISHA

Well, I don't know, baby. We got a few more boxes to put into the car, then we really need to be on our way.

KEENAN

I can finish, babe.

JACOB

Yeah, Mom, I'll only be about ten to fifteen minutes tops. I promise.

Keisha is a bit hesitant. Something doesn't feel right. Her gut says no, but she sees how excited Jacob is. She can't say no.

KEISHA

Ok, Jacob, but hurry back, ok?

JACOB

Yes! I will, Mom, thanks.

Jacob kisses his mother on the cheek, then quickly runs off down the sidewalk. All smiles, he stops running when he gets about half a block away from Mr. Tony's and starts walking, as he continues to stare down and look at his book. Suddenly, a black SUV pulls up alongside him with smoked-out tinted windows.

SLOW MOTION

The passenger side window slowly rolls down. Jacob turns to look and sees a black man reaching inside his jacket pocket. Jacob starts freezing in fear. He's afraid he's about to get shot, his heart is pounding outside of his chest. As the man pulls out an object, Jacob turns to run.

END SLOW MOTION

BLACK MAN

What's up, Jacob? Let me get your autograph, little man.

Jacob looks back and sees that the man is holding a PEN. He takes a deep breath. The man pulls out a copy of Jacob's book.

JACOB

Oh, okay cool!

Jacob happily walks over to the SUV and signs the man's book.

BLACK MAN

Thanks, Jacob. This is a good book, man. I'm going to order two more copies for my boys, man. Keep speaking your truth!

JACOB

(smiling)

Thank you, thanks for the support!

The man smiles as the SUV pulls off.

INT. BOOK STORE -- A FEW MONTHS LATER

A large crowd is gathered inside the bookstore for Jacob's book signing. Large best-selling author posters of Jacob and his book are posted around the store. Jacob sits at a panel table with a microphone in hand while his mother and Jack sit beside him. A few reporters are present; photographers take pictures of the event. Miss Collins, Keenan, and Sara can be seen in the crowd. A well-groomed Pruval can be seen standing in the back. His job is done; he smiles as he turns to walk away.

(whispering)   **JACK**

This is your moment, Jacob, are you ready?

Jacob nods his head. Jack gestures him to proceed.

JACOB

Hello, everyone!

The crowd replies, "Hello, Jacob."

JACOB (CONT'D)

I dedicate this book to my friend Kenny. Um, I just want to thank everyone for buying my book and for supporting me. It means the world to my mom and I.

Everyone CLAPS!

JACOB (CONT'D)

Before I sign everyone's book, I just
wanted to take a brief moment and read a
short passage from my book.

Jacob clears his throat as he opens to a passage in his book.

JACOB (CONT'D)

"Where I'm from, crimes are committed on
a daily basis and it's a stigma to tell
the truth or to speak up at all. Since
when did telling the truth and speaking
up for the safety of your community make
you a snitch? In my view, you should be
looked upon as a liberator against crime
and unjust acts of violence and not as
if you had some type of contagious
disease for doing what's right. Why do
we let evildoers put us in a box and
force us to play by their rules? You
are not the product of your environment
unless you choose to be. In my opinion,
no one in their right mind loves living
in the ghetto, but many won't lift a
finger to pull themselves out. Why?
It's past time for people to band
together and take back their communities
from gangs, drugs, and senseless
violence. By the grace of God, my
mother and I were able to make it out,
and I'm so thankful. We all have a
talent, so let's find or rediscover
them. I promise, it's not far from
you."

Everyone cheers and claps for Jacob. Some people are overcome with emotion. Everyone lines up, as Jacob starts autographing people's book. Keisha leans over and kisses Jacob on the cheek.

FADE OUT:

"YOUNG SOLDIER"

Your home is the ghetto
The only friend you ever see is your shadow…
The female gender is disrespected, young and old…
You got big dreams, but you feel trapped because
you're ashamed of where you're at…
Surrounded by filthy roaches and dirty rats…
I know you ask yourself why
just keep your head up, young soldier, and don't cry…
If you look outside, you won't see any kids at play
but different drug addicts roaming the streets night and day.
You got 7-year-olds selling Glocks
the only music you hear when you sleep is gun shots…
And the thing that angers you the most
is that the government knows
but is too busy sticking their nose
in other countries' ghettos…
At night, you crawl deep under your covers
wondering where's your mother…
Squeezing the bible tightly as you say your prayers
asking the Lord why…
Just keep your head up, young soldier
and don't cry.

GLOSSARY

INT. - Interior, inside scene.

EXT. – Exterior, outside scene.

FADE IN. – Dissolve to a color, usually the opening and ending scene.

FLASHBACK. – Transition to an earlier moment in time.

PRESENT TIME. – Signals the end of a flashback scene or scenes.

INTERCUT. – Showing scenes simultaneously back and forth for a few moments.

MONTAGE. – A series of scenes or images, showing the passage of time.

O. S. – Off-Screen or Off-Camera. Normally, when a character or noise is heard, but not seen, no visual.

Parenthetical. – To emphasize a particular emotion or stress a point.

V. O. – Voice Over (narration).

CUT TO. – A quick transition from one scene to the next, mostly used for a dramatic effect.

DISSOLVE TO. – Where one scene fades out slowly into another scene.

CONTINUOUS. – No interruptions in the passage of time. Continuation of scene, event, or time.

SMASH CUT. – A sharp transition, from scene to the next.

BEAT. – Signals a pause within the dialogue or action.

GET TO KNOW THE AUTHOR

TRAVIS PEAGLER is a very unique individual, from being the youngest of seven kids, raised partially in low-income apartments on the east side of Dayton, OH until the age of nine. Humble beginnings in growing in a somewhat multi-racial neighborhood gave Travis an inimitable perspective on life at a very young age.

His imagination has always been his outlet. Thinking back to grade school when he was in an uncomfortable situation or when he didn't handle a conflict well, Travis would always replay the scene back in his mind where things played out the way he wished. An innate defense mechanism, he assumes. But, that's when he discovered that he was a quick thinker and could really make up some cool stories, with his wild and vivid imagination. Slowly, he began to embrace this wonderful gift of mastering words, and creating stories and make-believe characters.

Travis loves telling original stories; something he truly feels has been lacking since the 80s and early 90s, in his opinion. There are so many great stories, floating around in the atmosphere, that are yet to be told. His aim is to catch as many as he can and share them with the world.

On a professional level, Travis is a Military Veteran and has worked in the finance industry for almost ten years. He has two kids and has been married for 14 years. With any free time, Travis enjoys lifting weights, dancing with his daughter, playing games with his son, and going to the movies with his wife. Travis has resided in Indianapolis, IN with his family for 13 years.

Keep up with Travis for future books, giveaways, etc. at the following:

www.TravisPeagler.com
Email: TravisWriter@TravisPeagler.com
amazon.com/author/travispeagler
Facebook, @ScriptNovels
Instagram, @TravisWriterPeagler
Twitter, @PeaglerTravis

ME AT AGE 7

www.TravisPeagler.com

Made in the USA
Las Vegas, NV
27 November 2020